VICTORIA
GRANDOLET

A Novel by

Henry Bellamann

SIMON AND SCHUSTER · NEW YORK

1944

THIRD PRINTING

About the Appearance of Books in Wartime

A recent ruling by the War Production Board has curtailed the use of paper by book publishers in 1943.

In line with this ruling and in order to conserve materials and manpower, we are co-operating by:

1. Using lighter-weight paper which reduces the bulk of our books substantially.
2. Printing books with smaller margins and with more words to each page. Result: fewer pages per book.

Slimmer and smaller books will save paper and plate metal and labor. We are sure that readers will understand the publishers' desire to co-operate as fully as possible with the objectives of the War Production Board and our government.

MANUFACTURED IN THE UNITED STATES OF AMERICA
BY AMERICAN BOOK—STRATFORD PRESS, INC., N. Y.

To my friends

Paul and Adelaide Adams

This story is entirely fictional. There is no White Cloud. There are no Grandolets. There are, however, in Louisiana, houses of comparable magic; and there are Louisiana families of similar archaic temper.

I am grateful to many Louisiana friends and to my innumerable relatives for quantities of Louisiana talk which contributed to the substance and atmosphere of this story.

H. B.

ONE

THE BLAZING LOUISIANA SUMMER lay like a quivering tide over the wide flat land. The heat seemed to pour down from above, from all around, and to thrust up from the white, dusty road. This road traversed a countryside which appeared to be wholly deserted. A few abandoned cabins with sagging roofs stood in clumps of chinaberry trees, but there were no fences, no branching lanes, no signs of life.

Enormous oaks, heavily draped in moss, looked more like ruins of trees than living things.

The road led into the swamps. On both sides the dense walls of green stood close. Cypress trees grew from the still, dark water, their slender trunks rising branchless and straight in a desperate reach for the sun. Bay and magnolia, maples and towering tulip trees, struggled for room, the whole entangled and snarled and enmeshed in a mass of swinging, climbing, twisting vines. There were streaks of red-flowering creepers laced back and forth among the gray branches, and overhead the rustle and flutter of wings.

Mile after mile it was the same, broken only at long intervals by ink-black bayous covered with emerald-green water hyacinth. Tens of thousands of palmettos crowded among the trees with an uncanny look of moving life. They appeared to be a multitude of hands lifted in acclamation—or warning.

The fleckless, burnished, intolerable sky was a deep wistaria blue. The still, waiting aspect of the whole country had a look of eternity about it.

A small rubber-tired buggy, drawn by a wild-looking chestnut pair, was speeding eastward on this narrow, straight, lonely road—the road from Oquipah to the river and to White Cloud plantation. The driver held the lines with a firm, expert hand. He was a young man, perhaps twenty-five or -six, lean and brown, seeming at once lazy and alert in the disconcerting way of so many men of this region. This was Niles Grandolet, owner of White Cloud.

The girl sitting beside him was his bride. They had been married ten days before in Virginia.

Niles Grandolet had gone there to attend the graduation of his cousin, Flora Vélazy, from Fairfield Seminary. His headlong and slightly crazy courtship of Flora's roommate, Victoria Dunstan, began about an hour after his arrival.

Niles grinned now at the kaleidoscopic recollection of that mad week. A slight, persistent sense of question sent a tremor of disquiet along his nerves. Here, coming again into his own familiar country, his attention and his fancy began to turn right side up. A kind of accustomed quiet came to him, and that quiet was disturbing. He had not thought, really, of what had happened, until this minute. He, Niles Grandolet, was married.

Two weeks ago when he had driven along this way, he had not so much as heard of her. Even now, he knew very little.

He glanced quickly at Victoria. His bright, amber-colored eyes warmed at the sight of her cool, silvery beauty. Victoria was slender, and soft, and somewhat voluptuous-looking, but her sensuous contours and colorings were tempered in effect by a quiet and instinctive control. Her eyes, wide apart, and slanting ever so slightly, were dark and shadowy, somewhere between blue and gray, and in arresting contrast to her almost snowy complexion and ashy-blond hair. Niles' quick remembering flashed back again over those few days in Virginia. As mad as could be!

"Maybe it was because I didn't go to the Carnival this year," he said aloud.

Victoria turned her eyes slowly toward him. "What did you say?"

He laughed. "Talking to myself."

The buggy rolled evenly onto a narrow wooden bridge. The water of the bayou lay still, burnished in the afternoon sun. Niles gazed at it with sparkling delight. It was his world, every phase of it familiar and treasured. His glance ran over it as if he were reading a well-loved book.

Inside of herself, Victoria drew back from it. She looked at the strange trees, the creepy, dangerous swamp, the lonely, inhospitable reach of the whole landscape, and wondered if she could ever come to view it as a known and understood thing.

A wave of unsettling emotion went over her with a sickening slowness. It was not homesickness, it was not dread, it was not terror. She was not able to define it. Perhaps it was the utter strangeness of everything. There was no single aspect where her strained attention might rest in comfort for a single moment. And the man beside her: he was no less strange than this strange land. She knew nothing about him, his house, or his people, nothing of his way of thought, what he might value or despise, what he might cherish or refuse.

Victoria set her mind to resist the dismay that was slowly

invading it. She had always valued courage, she had imagined that she was courageous. Doubtless, she would have opportunity to try herself.

They had come up from New Orleans on an indescribably casual train. From the moment the ragged country replaced the squalid huddle fringing the city, she had felt that she was moving farther and farther from everything she had known. The land, the houses, the people, all were strange. She had had to ask Niles innumerable questions. What were those dark-green umbrellalike trees? Chinaberry. Why did the yards have no grass? Just a local custom—so you could see snakes, maybe. He laughed at that. They had passed several small cemeteries. Why were those brick structures over the graves? Those are really vaults aboveground. Why? Because this soil is pretty near all water: dig a grave and it's full of water before you can use it! She had shuddered at that. It made the very soil sound inimical. She had said so, and Niles had glanced curiously at her. The soil *is* unfriendly; you have to watch it. We have all sorts of things down here, he had said. It isn't like New England, where you build and live *with* the land. Here you build *against* it. You guard against the life that creeps through it and on it. There is quicksand, there are floods, there are things that bite, and lots of us still believe the air is full of fever. That isn't so, of course. But it is true of this country that you live in it rather than with it. You'll get used to it, and you'll love it as all of us do, and then you couldn't live away from it.

She had been a little wide-eyed at all of that. She felt the challenge that lay behind Niles' light words.

And then it seemed to her that these must be quite special people—people who set themselves against danger and threat.

There was a hint of romance about the whole idea. For a moment the strangeness became allure. For a moment she thrilled to her expectation of whatever might await her.

They left the train at Oquipah, where the buggy was waiting for them. There were Negroes who had brought the buggy and a wagon for baggage. There were endless and confusing outcries of delight from them at the sight of Niles, who responded with a badinage she could not understand. Every word he uttered sent them into ecstasies of laughter. She was bewildered. All of the Negroes looked alike.

"We'll soon be there, honey." Niles flicked the tasseled whip across the sweating horses which took the road as if in flight. "Tired out?"

She shook her head. "I'm just looking."

The horses thundered over another bridge. Another wide bayou glistened in the afternoon sun. It reached back into the swamps on both sides, disappearing under low-hanging jungles of green.

Niles pointed with his whip. "Tete Rouge Bayou. White Cloud begins on the other side."

Across the bridge there was the same blind tangle of green and black. But Niles looked quickly from side to side with a new light in his eyes.

"White Cloud," he said softly.

Victoria squinted ahead. There still seemed no turning in the road as far as she could see, and no break in the massive fortress of green.

"Niles, how big a place is White Cloud?"

"The plantation, you mean?"

"Yes."

"I don't know, exactly. Between four and five thousand acres. There are two other places, Far Félice and Wyandotte. We don't own Wyandotte—just lease it."

"Goodness! Isn't that an awful lot?"

"Plenty. Plenty when you have to look after it. Keeps you at it all the time. I thought I ought not to leave it just at this time, but—Flora insisted. I'm glad I went, though."

He turned toward her and smiled. She smiled in return but said nothing. The faintest possible shadow of question darkened his eyes for a moment. "Gee!" he said, and laughed aloud. It was a gay, infectious, flattering laugh that took in the listener and seemed to make a partnership in some irrepressible pleasure. "Gee!" he repeated.

The sunlight was already slanting and the heat had lessened when they came out into the open country. As far as they could see, the rippling fields lay flat as a table top.

"Cane, honey." Niles made a circling gesture.

"Oh."

"It's sugar, but it's White Cloud's bread and butter."

"I have so much to learn, Niles. I didn't know what sugar cane looked like."

Just ahead, a long white house with galleries stood far back from the road.

"Is that——"

"That's old Tom Ward's house. Ward is the plantation overseer."

Victoria bit her lip. She had thought it must be White Cloud itself.

"Look, Vicky—see yonder, straight ahead?"

A huge, billowy grove of trees loomed in the midst of the treeless fields. "That's White Cloud, honey. Home."

"I can't see anything, Niles."

[6]

"Trees hide the house. In a minute now—look, you can see the roof."

Victoria shaded her eyes. A small forest of red-brick chimneys began to show above an enormous complication of colored slate. Then the gleam of a white colonnade flashed for an instant through an opening in the grove, but even that instant gave Victoria an impression of something remote and proud and not altogether friendly.

Her heart beat fast and hard. The light, turning pale gold, spread a curious enchantment over the landscape. It was—she thought for a moment—it was the same light that hangs like a spell over the background of old Italian paintings. It was a distant, unfamiliar light, rare and beautiful, and wholly alien. The trees were motionless in that light as if they had always stood so, jealously and anciently on guard.

The road ran close to a tall, leafy hedge. Still no further sight of the house showed through.

"This is really coming in the back way. The entrance to White Cloud was originally from the river—the house faces the river, you know."

"But where is the river?"

"There, straight ahead. Only that's the levee you see. The levee was built right through our front yard. There isn't a river landing any more—not anywhere near the house."

The buggy swerved through an opening in the hedge and rolled into a wide park. There were hedges and great trees trailing gray moss, tall flowering bushes, and here and there brick pedestals supporting classic statues, weather-stained and streaked, pallid under the late sun. The drive rounded a circle of glossy shrubbery.

"Here we are!" There was an odd pulse in Niles' voice. Victoria had not heard it there before. She looked, and gasped.

[7]

"Oh, Niles!"

"Isn't it an old beauty?"

"I never saw anything so lovely!"

"Just wait until you really see it."

"You didn't tell me."

"Oh, you can't describe White Cloud."

The vast house stood high on a rose-brick foundation. Curved stairs swept up to a bewildering series of terraces, galleries, colonnades, and wrought-iron balconies. The whole structure seemed to float—like a mirage. Over it all was an air of grace and lightness which in no way lessened the impact of its certain pride.

Niles pulled the horses to a stop. "Just for a single minute, Victoria, I want you to look at it. Like it?"

She laid her hand on his arm. *"Like* it?"

The little shadow that had lain across his face from time to time this day vanished completely.

"It's home, honey."

Victoria gazed at the house intently. The long rows of windows with faded green shutters, the great wings on both sides of the central building, the deep shadows behind the tall, fluted columns—nothing seemed real. There was no sign of life anywhere. White Cloud stood wrapped in the pomp of an unbroken silence.

"I want to say it now, Victoria, before we get there. 'Welcome to White Cloud.'"

She was a little pale as she answered, and her voice was husky. "Thank you, Niles."

Niles slackened the reins and the horses leaped forward. As they clattered to a stop, half a dozen Negroes sprang up from nowhere, and Niles helped her out to a huge square

[8]

block of granite. He bowed gaily and took her by the hand. "Mrs. Grandolet——"

A gay voice with a note of excitement in it sounded above their heads.

"Not that stair, Niles—the left one—the left one!"

Victoria looked up. A white-haired little woman leaned over the balustrade, smiling and beckoning. She waited at the top of the stairs and held out her hands.

"Welcome home, Victoria."

"Vicky, this is Aunt Lucie."

"Of course—I knew."

A tall, exaggeratedly thin old man stood behind Aunt Lucie Niles kissed him on both cheeks.

"My boy!" He held Niles close for a moment.

"Grandfather, this is Victoria."

"I am glad to welcome Niles' wife to White Cloud."

He held out his hand, and barely brushed her cheek with his lips.

"Thank you." Victoria half whispered the words.

"It is a great event in our lives, and in our family—a new mistress at White Cloud. It has been a long time——" The words trailed away. The old man's round brown eyes, set deep under the heavily lined brow, continued to look steadily at her.

"But—come in, children, come in!"

He took Victoria's arm.

"Aunt Lucie," Niles stopped on the threshold. "Why did you say the left stair?"

"Why, Niles, surely you know. It's an old sort of story—a custom, I guess. Brides always enter White Cloud by the left stair." She hesitated a moment, then added, "The dead go out by the other one."

[9]

As she crossed the threshold Victoria had a confused impression of a wide, lofty space somewhat shadowy and indistinct. A staircase lay at the far end of this floor, flanked by two doors through which she glimpsed a court and more galleries. Just now several Negro faces were silhouetted in each opening. Again there was a medley of outcry and greeting to Niles.

Aunt Lucie did not pause but mounted at once to the first circular gallery. There were rows of portraits in the half-dark.

From the instant Victoria had entered the front door of White Cloud her attention had been held by one object. Now, she paused, her hand on the polished railing of the balustrade.

The center hall was open to the top of the building and circled with galleries. In this well an enormous chandelier swung by a slender bronze chain from the high crossbeams of the roof.

Aunt Lucie paused, too. "One of the traveling Grandolets brought it from Scotland early in the nineteenth century," she said, nodding as if in agreement with Victoria's unspoken admiration.

It was like a huge cascade of jewels, ropes and chains and clusters, glittering and flashing as it swung gently, almost imperceptibly, on its long chain. From the many slender arms arose a veritable chevaux-de-frise of thin crystal spikes.

"It is never still," Aunt Lucie remarked, "never."

The heavy mass of bronze and fire turned slightly and quivered as if deep tremors in the house and in the earth under the house stirred it. Indeed, as it trembled, its faceted gems glowing and sparkling with blue and green and orange and ruby lights, it seemed to be a symbol of the life of this beautiful house—perhaps the heart of that life, brilliant and changeful, watchful and—mocking.

Victoria drew her shoulders up a little and turned back to Aunt Lucie.

"These are your rooms, Victoria." Aunt Lucie opened a door into a dim, high-ceilinged room, pearl white and shimmering with old brocades. Through an archway Victoria saw a second room with a great canopied bed.

"All of the mistresses of White Cloud have occupied these rooms. I am sorry there was no time to have anything done. Even the hangings aren't down for the summer. And you'll probably find a lot of my things tucked away here and there, but we'll get straightened out pretty soon."

"Did you——"

"I've lived in these rooms since Niles was a baby," Aunt Lucie rattled on quickly. "His mother died shortly after he was born, you know, and I had to take charge."

"But don't you want to stay in here? You must be used to——"

"Oh, my dear!" Aunt Lucie looked genuinely shocked. "My dear!" She seemed to have the breath taken out of her by the suggestion. "It is a tradition of the house, Victoria. As I said, the mistresses of White Cloud *always* occupy these rooms. Niles was born in that room—in that bed; and his father and his grandfather. Dear me!"

Aunt Lucie opened one of the French windows. "There, my dear, look! It is one of the finest views of the river I know of anywhere. The balcony runs all around the house—you may have noticed. And now, this is Orlou. She will be your personal maid."

"Howdy, ma'am."

Victoria stared for just a fleeting second. The gaunt woman standing there had materialized, as it seemed, out of the air at Aunt Lucie's word. Victoria had not heard a step or a rustle.

Orlou was a light café-au-lait complexioned woman, appearing neither young nor old. She wore a narrow, stiff-starched white dress, and a high white headcloth that had a decidedly Egyptian look. She stood perfectly still, her face impassive and her impenetrable black eyes steady.

Victoria inclined her head and smiled easily. Inside she was not quite comfortable, but the feeling was not definable.

Aunt Lucie bridged the moment. "Orlou has been here— well, she was born here, just like most of us, weren't you, Orlou?"

"Yes, ma'am."

Victoria nodded appreciation of Orlou's slightly emphatic reply.

"That's nice. I am sure Orlou and I shall get along perfectly."

"I'm proud to serve Mr. Niles' wife."

Orlou looked like some sort of priestess, Victoria thought, but there was something familiar in her expression. It teased at her attention for a moment.

"Orlou will unpack for you as soon as your trunks come. I know you will want to lie down for a little while."

Niles had come in quietly and stood leaning against the door frame. He laughed. "Aunt Lucie has met every crisis in her life by lying down for a little while."

Aunt Lucie laughed, too, but wagged her head sagely. "You will find it a great help, Victoria, especially with this climate and—the Grandolets."

"Vicky, don't let Aunt Lucie and Orlou scare you with tales about the Grandolets. They make them up. We're simple country people."

Orlou's somber gaze shifted a little. She almost smiled. Again, Victoria thought she looked familiar. All at once she remembered a print that hung in her father's study. She narrowed her eyes a little, regarding Orlou. Orlou looked like Michelangelo's *Cumaean Sibyl*. Rather magnificent—for one's maid, she thought.

"I think everything is here, Victoria. You have some things in your valise, haven't you, for a change after that hot drive? I do hope it didn't tire you out too much. Twenty miles on a June day. My, my! Orlou will attend you now, my dear. I do hope you'll be comfortable."

Niles was watching Aunt Lucie as she prattled on, never waiting for comment or an answer. There was half a question in his eye, too, but nothing in Aunt Lucie's face or manner answered it.

"Come on, Niles. Let Victoria rest a while. I have a thousand things to ask you. I never do know just what to do when you are away. Come along. Victoria, we have supper about half-past seven—if it's ready."

A warm glow still lingered out of doors when Victoria came down the stairs, but all of the lower floor was brightly lighted. There were tall candles set in innumerable lusters, and the great chandelier twinkled with a starry brilliance as it swayed slightly in the breathless stillness. Niles came out from a side hall.

"Oh, there you are."

"Niles!" She caught her breath with a little gasp as she looked about her. "This is the most beautiful house——"

He seemed pleased. "Yes, it is. Though, I must say it looks better at night. You don't see the shabbiness, the worn-out places. But, I guess we wouldn't change even that. Not much, anyway."

"It's magical."

"The candles are all in your honor. We don't do this every night."

Aunt Lucie came down the stairs at that moment. "Of course it's in her honor. My, my, I feel quite gay." But there was a faintly wistful tone in her voice as she spoke. Victoria was certain Aunt Lucie was not gay.

"Come into the library, children. Father will be there."

The library was dimly lighted by a pair of silver lamps with opaque glass shades.

"You here, Father?"

The old gentleman arose from his chair. He bowed slightly to Victoria. "I hope you are rested after your long drive."

"Oh, it was nothing, really. I was so interested in seeing Louisiana for the first time."

"Rather unlike New Hampshire, I imagine."

"But New Hampshire is beautiful, too."

Grandfather Grandolet touched a slender decanter. "Niles!"

"Yes, sir."

Niles filled the glasses.

Again the old gentleman inclined slightly toward Victoria. He lifted his glass. "To your good health, your happiness— and a long life at White Cloud."

"Thank you." Victoria felt a slight tremor in her knees. There was something in the tone and in the set formality of the words that sounded like a sentence.

The dining room opened and a soft Negro voice said, casually, "Supper's ready, Miss Lucie."

As they took their places at the huge oval table, Victoria had a sensation as of weight, as if a hand rested for a moment on her shoulder.

The long, high room glittered with candles in crystal candelabra, the table was heaped with massive silver, the linen was old and fine and soft, the food was rich and unfamiliar. Moment by moment everything seemed more and more strange. Conversation was easy and inconsequential, though the manner of the hour was formal—formal, but not festive.

Victoria considered Niles' grandfather Julien with growing interest, but she observed Aunt Lucie with more care.

Aunt Lucie seemed a bit fluttery, but, nevertheless, easy of manner. She was brown-eyed like her father, and Niles, and the set and carriage of her head were like theirs, proud and assured. It rather contradicted her extreme gentleness of manner. Victoria thought for a moment. She had seen that exact combination of disparate qualities before. The headmistress at Fairfield Seminary had it. She identified it in her mind with the habit of easy command. She believed it was the manner of people of consequence everywhere. Aunt Lucie ate with appetite and interest. She explained the origin and character of the many bewildering dishes, seemingly served in endless sequence and staggering quantity.

Grandfather Julien, in contrast, seemed not to eat at all. When he did actually eat something, he did it with an air of complete indifference, rather as if he were feeding someone else. He appeared not to notice anyone, but Victoria felt his gaze on her whenever she looked away.

Once she caught his eye in the midst of one of Aunt Lucie's complicated stories. He flashed a quick look of amusement in her direction.

"My child, you will have quite a time getting used to us."

"I—I don't believe I shall."

"It's the way we talk."

Aunt Lucie broke in gaily. "How *do* we talk, Father?"

"Forever." He turned to Victoria. "It's like this, Victoria. We haven't anything new to say. We tell the same stories over

[15]

and over, repeat the same remarks, rehash the ten-times-familiar histories. That's why it doesn't make any difference whether we begin in the middle or at the end. Notice Lucie, now. She goes backward or forward or sideways in her stories. It doesn't make any difference since we know all of them, anyway. But you'll be bewildered, at first."

"Father always derides our ways, Victoria. It is his idea of domestic humor. I'm sure we're as queer as can be, but——" Aunt Lucie arose.

Niles linked arms with Victoria. "You'll develop your own brand of peculiarity after a while, and then——"

"You'll be a full-fledged Grandolet." Grandfather Julien never seemed really to smile, but a faintly malicious expression replaced his set look of detachment. He had a slightly Mephistophelian cast, Victoria thought, but despite this and his remote severity, she felt in him the rapid and continuous play of a lively imagination. He was old and very frail, but there was some kind of fabulous inner vivacity animating him to his finger tips.

Aunt Lucie led them to the drawing room.

This enormous double room had an unused look, as if it had long ago withdrawn from any participation in the life of the house.

Niles' eyes danced as he watched Victoria. "Terrible room, isn't it?"

"Why, Niles, no."

"Nonsense. You live here now, you don't have to be polite. It *is* a terrible room. Even Aunt Lucie thinks so, and she loves the worst of the place."

Aunt Lucie smiled gently. "I don't think it is terrible, not quite. It's just—well, it was built for another kind of life in another day. I imagine long ago, when there were great house parties at White Cloud, this must have been a very gay and useful room."

Victoria took quick note of the high molded ceilings, the stately paneling, and the chill marble mantels. The floor was covered with a faded Aubusson, and the clusters of ornate sofas and chairs had been grouped in an effort to break the space into small hospitable islands.

"You know, Vicky," Niles waved his coffee cup recklessly in a gesture of inclusion. "All of this doesn't go together. The house is gracious and pure, but this infernal Louis Philippe furniture was just a part of the dreadful taste in decoration which seemed somehow to flourish side by side with the superlative taste of the occasional builder."

"Oh, Niles——" Aunt Lucie tried to break in.

"True, Aunt Lucie. And don't forget that even White Cloud is an exception."

The talk ran on about other places. Niles was witty, but Aunt Lucie hotly disagreed. Victoria knew nothing about architectural values or period furniture. She listened, a bit bewildered by the apparent fervor of the discussion. Grandfather Grandolet said nothing. From time to time Victoria was aware of his bright, steady eyes, seeming to regard her without question and almost without interest.

She sipped her bitter black coffee, trying with all her mind to realize that she was married to Niles Grandolet, that this was home, that she was not a guest but the mistress of this bewildering, disturbing house. It was a vain effort. The feeling persisted that presently—in a moment—she would go away, that she would find herself back in her little room at school with Flora Vélazy, or back in the tidy, tight little rectory in New Hampshire.

She lost the thread of the talk altogether. She was trying

to check the vertiginous rush of new impressions for even a minute, trying to seize one or two sensations, to hold them until she found herself. An unfamiliar perfume was in the air, seemingly light at first, then changing a little, then dizzily cloying.

"What is it, Niles?"

"What is what, honey?"

"Is it some kind of flower?"

Niles stared for an instant. Then he laughed and sniffed. "Magnolias, Vicky."

"Oh, I—I didn't know. I never smelled them before."

Aunt Lucie cried out in amaze. "My dear child, nothing you could have said would have—how do I want to say it?— would show how far away you come——"

Niles yelped. "Look out, Aunt Lucie. That sentence is getting the better of you. Yep, Vicky, you're a foreigner, all right. Come over here to the window. There's a whole grove of magnolias off this side."

Aunt Lucie and her father arose. "I think Father and I will be off to bed, my dears. We've had an exciting day, you know." She kissed Victoria on the cheek.

"Good night, Aunt Lucie."

"Good night, children."

Niles thrust aside the hangings at one of the windows and they stepped out on the gallery. The air was heavy with the scent of many flowers.

"It's heavenly, Niles, isn't it?"

"I love it, honey. I couldn't live anywhere else. Life is prodigal down here. Everything grows like crazy—especially the things you wish wouldn't. I couldn't bear your skimpy kind of country. Hope you don't mind if I say so?"

She shook her head. "I know what you mean."

"Come here, I want to show you something." He crossed the gallery to a balustraded stair that led down to a wide, open terrace. At the far corner he turned. "Now look!"

Victoria did not speak. From this place the house stood high and clear in the bright moonlight. One could see both the east front and south colonnades, rising with an indescribable lightness, as pure and as ethereal as cloud.

After a moment Victoria said softly, "I see why it was called White Cloud."

"Yes, I guess old Quintin Grandolet was something of a poet."

"Let's don't go in right away, Niles."

"All right, honey. Here's a seat."

He put his arm about her and drew her close. She stiffened for a moment and then let her head rest on his shoulder.

Nothing, she thought, could ever make White Cloud seem real. The gleaming white lines of columns, of pilaster and frieze, the contrasting black of the dense trees with their mournful banners of moss, the warm sweet air, the stillness that took on presently the multitudinous murmur of night—none of it was real. It was like a spell, enchanting the senses.

She felt a sudden rush of exultation. She understood what Niles meant—*I couldn't live anywhere else.* Nor could she, she thought—not now.

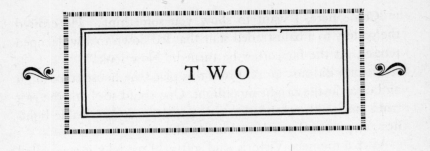

TWO

No ONE UNDERSTOOD WHY Victoria liked to walk along the
levee. She had not understood the fancy herself—not at first.
But as the days went by it became something of a compulsion.

"Watch out for the snakes, Victoria, and don't go far—not
out of sight of the house." There was a note of gravity in Niles'
voice.

Here on the levee—a great grassy embankment following the
contour of the river—she had a view of the house set against
an almost black background of ancient trees. On the other
side the great Mississippi swung in a mighty curve. Between
the river and the levee itself was a wide stretch of willow-
grown swamp.

The contrast was dramatic.

The river, the swamp, and the heavy woods on the east
bank were all wild and primitive—nature in an uncompromising mood of cruelty and indifference to man. The elemental
force of the wide waters which seemed to swim forward with
such irresistible power fascinated her.

The house looked almost fragile viewed from here. It arose,
dreamlike and delicate—its powder-white façade and airy proportions an expression of so much that man had struggled to
achieve. It had an air of courage, of calm and assurance. So had

the spirit of a family and a people said its word against the jungle and the savagery of an inhospitable nature. It was, she thought, a symbol of man's place in the universe—setting the frailty of beauty there, encircled by something wilder than a wilderness, holding the strength of a vision against every material assault. At such moments the house inspired her, but at other times it disturbed her, cowed her, even, and lifted itself against her.

That was why she had to go outside of it, walk up and down the path on the levee, and try to establish a perspective.

In spite of every effort to orient herself, there were days when she felt more and more a stranger to the place and the people in it. Everyone was kind. Niles was gay. He made endless jokes and told her funny stories of the parish people. Aunt Lucie initiated her gradually into the intricacies of family history. Grandfather Julien dwelt formally on the regional stories. Orlou embroidered fact with legend, colored and shaped all stories with superstition and dark additions which sometimes made Victoria's blood chill in her veins.

No one ever mentioned the word aristocrat. But Victoria came quickly to see that here was an old, old order of being and thinking—older than Louisiana or America, something perhaps more Spanish than French, and altered little or not at all by infusions of English blood and belief. A family personality began to emerge and take shape. It was a complex and difficult personality—fastidious, exacting, thinned by time, but almost malevolently alive—perhaps cruel.

The visible witness of this and the defined expression of it was the house itself—White Cloud—beautiful and still and insolent in its regal indifference to anything not in harmony with it.

Victoria had felt a rising pride in the place as she came to see it more clearly—and then, she hardly knew how it came about, whether gradually or in some moment of clairvoyance, one day as she came toward it she felt that it was her enemy. She had stopped and looked up at the singular grace and balance of the whole structure. It seemed to gaze out across the park, out beyond, over her head to some secret distance, some secret and splendid vision in which it was a lofty inheritor. It seemed to say that she—Victoria Lynn Dunstan—was not a sharer in that destiny.

She stood quite still, looking steadily at the outline of balconies, porticoes, and terraces. This was morbid nonsense, she told herself. It was absurd to suppose that a house *could* be one's enemy. She was imagining things, and she knew the source of these imaginings. The more she had felt the impact of the Grandolet personality, the composite personality of the house and the people in it, the more keenly had she searched her mind for a measure of herself. She had known long ago that a day would come when that measure would have to be taken. The thought, the searching, the bitter probe of her own questioning took her back to a November day long ago. Her father, the Reverend Arthur Lynn Dunstan, had told her the story about herself. She was still a child when he told her, but she had been a precocious child. She understood the full implication of the story at once. *She did not know who she was.* No one knew. Not even the Reverend Arthur Lynn Dunstan, who declined to tell her where she came from. They had talked it over. A rush of humiliation had engulfed every other feeling. She was different—different from all the other children—shamefully different. This man on whose knees she was sitting was no more to her than any stranger in the street. His arm about her, the caressing warmth of his effort at consolation, these were the gestures and the signs of an affection for which she must be grateful. She owed a debt in return for them—for everything, food, clothes, even for the rather austere shelter of a house which was *his* house—not really her home.

She held very still that day. She did not move her head which lay close against his face.

Then as her curiosity had troubled her more and more she had beset him with questions. Here she met a new and unexpected resistance.

"You are a good girl, Victoria; it is enough for you to know that. If I knew anything of importance about you I would not withhold it, you must believe me. It is simply that I wish to spare you idle speculation and prevent you from engaging in vain searching in the future. You cheered the life of your foster mother. You have her name—Victoria. I wish she had lived to see you grow up. I—I am happy to call you my daughter. But please let me say again, don't make useless efforts to find out anything about yourself. I can assure you truthfully that no one knows any more than I have told you. I must ensure your future peace of mind, my dear."

Victoria knew in that moment that she ought to be touched and grateful. She considered a little the absence of proper and conventional emotions. She felt, instead, a sort of rage. It was a strange rage. She knew that, too. It was like a climate of the mind. She wondered if it would ever change, or would she live always in its curious twilight—a twilight broken only by fitful and wavering flashes from unknown sources.

The bright picture of White Cloud faded from her vision and she saw with unpleasant clearness the tidy little study where she had sat that November afternoon. She had almost lost herself in speculation—the very speculation against which Dr. Dunstan had warned her.

"How many people know?" she had asked the question bluntly. The slight change in his expression told her that he did not like the question.

But he had answered her gently, "No one, I fancy. We brought you here to Glaston as a baby. We did not think it necessary to say you were not our own. Your mother was many years younger than I, and no one suspected, or even troubled to think about it—so far as I know."

The last phrase disquieted her, but her scrutiny of his face did not waver. "Weren't you afraid of how I might turn out?"

"No more than I am now afraid of how any child may turn out. The human being—the human soul has unlimited possibilities, both for good and evil. I suppose I was no more uneasy about you than any parent is fearful for his child. You are intelligent, Victoria, and I think you are fine. These are important attributes. With them you can do anything."

You can do anything. The words lodged firmly. They became a magical formula for her—a sign. Since then she had said them over and over to herself with accents and overtones of appeasement, of promise, of support and exultation.

The mystery haunted her, harried her, and sometimes shook her with a swift onslaught of the same bafflement she had felt that day in her foster father's study.

But it was there and at that moment that she had made a precocious decision. She must *use* this, in some way. It must not use *her.*

If there was a mystery about her—then she was mysterious. As that feeling of mystery grew stronger in her she imposed it upon others. It was not long before people were saying, "That child of the rector's is a strange girl, isn't she?" Her quick, open frankness and her easy speech seemed to contradict the notion, and should have done so, but actually deepened the original impression.

But even then, she had set herself to hard thinking about herself. Other children were, just as she was, problems to themselves. The factors of known parentage and known ancestry were by no means certain guides to self-knowledge. Later, when she came under more advanced teaching at Fairfield she learned something about a directed introspection. All there was to be known about herself lay within her, and she alone had access to that region. She alone might know really what was there. She began a ruthless self-scrutiny that probed deep. What she discovered about herself she kept secret. No one even guessed at her strange journey into the hinterland of her own personality, or even anything of her need for such an examination.

Then she became more and more assured that she might use her peculiar circumstances even more effectively than she had ever guessed at as a child. She was certain that she might set for herself a larger freedom than others possessed. The known has always a ready-made pattern. The unknown might have limitless possibilities. Now, truly, she need place no bounds to what she might be or to what she might do.

You can do anything.

To the silent echo of those words she whispered eagerly and ambitiously, *Yes, yes!*

To go on, to go deeper and deeper into her own self, to use what she found, to be aware of a world where opportunity showed unexpectedly, to plan, to be decisive when moments for action arrived—all of this was an alluring method and a prospect constantly enchanted by its variety and its reach into the unknown.

Victoria looked coldly into the quick kaleidoscope of her

fancy. She must not, *must not* romanticize about anything. No, she told herself, she would be careful not to—this was not romanticizing, it was simply the planning of a strategy like the opening moves in chess. She liked to think of games, and of herself as a silent, enigmatic player.

Reflections, old and familiar, new and exciting, sped through her drifting, half-directed musing. She drew once more a curious strength from her secret. She straightened her slim shoulders. An odd smile touched her lips—odd because it was too old for her, too assured, too knowing.

Yes, all of that was long ago. She had believed as her school years went by that it was all safely out of sight, and buried beyond recovery. She had not counted on her own self. *She* knew, and she had to take her knowledge from its hiding place and stand it there before her consciousness, matching its power against the pervading and secret suggestions of White Cloud.

You can do anything.

The echo was a reassuring voice. She remembered once hearing her roommate, Flora Vélazy, say the same thing.

"Oh, but, Victoria, you are so talented. *You can do anything.*"

Could she? Could she? Could she match her strength, her self, against the power of White Cloud? For that it had a power over those who faced it, she did not doubt. But even Flora——

Her look softened a little when she thought of Flora. She had invited Flora to be her roommate merely to practice French, but Flora was the only girl she had ever really liked. Flora was little and dark, plump and vivacious—all round prettiness and rolling eyes, and quick gesticulation. Her warm Southern appearance set Victoria's silvery blondness in a sharp relief.

[26]

It had been a happy association, and for Victoria a most fortunate one.

Flora was popular on her own account, but her wealthy family and her intricate relationship to scores of Southern families counted heavily. Flora made herself a special champion of Victoria on all sorts of occasions. This was necessary, not because Victoria was disliked, but because she was reserved to the point of coldness, and because she was really an outsider. Southern girls understood each other so easily. It was too much trouble for them to attempt to fathom anything strange.

During the last two years Victoria's place in the school was different. She was noticed, she was included, she was discussed. She knew this and knew that Flora had been the effective agent of the change.

Victoria turned and resumed her walk. The late-afternoon light filled the park with magic. These old houses, these old places, had one quality that was always the same. They had the glamour, the unreality, of a stage setting. One remembered their brilliant and fabulous past, but they aroused also a feeling of expectancy. One was sure that presently something new and wonderful would come to pass.

Victoria lowered her sunshade. The great shadows lay across the levee and stretched out over the soft, plumy willows beyond. She was scarcely aware of the changing hour. Her effort at remembering went on by its own momentum. She was seeing again that fateful afternoon when her life had turned sharply into its new road. She had been reading and wondering a bit uneasily what she would do next. After Fairfield——

The door had flown open, banging against a dresser. Flora came in spreading an immediate air of confusion about her.

"Victoria, guess what!" Flora held the sheets of a letter pressed against her pouter-pigeon breast. "Guess what!"

"What now?" Victoria's tone was indulgent and amused.

"I'm so excited I could pop." Flora was still gasping for breath.

Victoria smiled. "Your brother is coming."

Flora shrieked with delight. "Victoria! You are so clever. How did you guess?"

"Not very hard to do, darling. You've been urging him for a month."

"Yes, of course; but that isn't half of it."

"No?"

"He's bringing somebody with him."

"Oh-h. Somebody important?"

Flora nodded. "Very."

"Somebody you haven't told me about?"

"Oh, I've mentioned him."

"Well—can it be told?"

"It's Niles Grandolet!"

"Niles Grandolet?"

"Yes. Isn't it glorious?"

"I don't know. Who is Niles Grandolet?"

"Oh, Victoria, I've told you about him time and time again —ever since I've known you."

"Dear, you've talked about hundreds of people. Cousins, cousins *of* cousins, second cousins, third cousins, aunts, uncles —you must be kin to most of Louisiana."

"I am—pretty near. That is——"

"All the nice people——"

"Of course."

Victoria smiled. "Go on. Tell me again about Niles Grandolet. How do you spell him?"

"G-r-a-n-d-o-l-e-t."

"Why do you pronounce the t?"

"Well, I guess so many people didn't know how to pronounce French names that we just have Anglicized most of them."

"We? Who is *we* this time?"

Flora ducked her head with a kind of childish embarrassment. "Honestly, it's funny, but Niles is a cousin, too."

"Oh!"

"But sort of distant."

"How distant?"

"You're teasing now, Victoria. I don't know quite truly. Our families are so mixed up 'way back. Some sort of double second cousin on my mother's side, or something like that."

"Your Southern relationships! I don't see how you ever keep them straight."

"We don't. When our kinfolks get too distant or too tacky we stop kissing. That's all."

"That's a classification, I suppose."

"Yes. Niles is a kissing cousin."

"Anything more?"

Flora colored. Surprisingly. She tossed her head a little. "He's pretty old."

"How old?"

"Twenty-six, maybe -seven."

"You funny thing. That isn't old."

"No. I guess I don't really think so."

Victoria leaned forward and rested her chin on her hand. "He is something to you, isn't he?"

"No. Truly."

"Honest?"

"Well——"

"I thought so. Well—what?"

"There was some talk in the family a couple of years ago but Aunt Hélène said we were such complicated cousins that we'd better not marry. She said it might not be healthy for our children."

Victoria fell back in her chair and laughed aloud. "Well, if you aren't the priceless——"

"Oh, there never was any engagement or anything like that. Our families just talk over all the young men we know."

"Were you in love with this Niles cousin?"

"Oh, no—I—I guess not."

"He's in love with you?"

"Goodness, no. He never even looked at me."

"Then what are you so excited about?"

"He's so wonderful. *You'll* like him."

"I think you like him yourself."

Flora flushed again, appeared to realize she was flushing, and was annoyed by it.

"Sure enough, now, Flora, how important is Niles Grandolet to you?"

"Not important in the least—that way. I'm just excited about seeing somebody from Louisiana."

Her tone was a bit weak and Victoria looked sharply at her.

Flora jumped up from the bed where she had been jouncing up and down as she talked. "Oh, I have a kodak of him. I forgot."

"You've always got a kodak, haven't you, of everyone you know?"

"I love kodaks." Flora was rummaging in an incredibly disordered dresser. The top was littered with ribbons, handkerchiefs, powder boxes, perfume bottles, and old letters. The mirror rim was jammed with kodak pictures.

"Here! I knew I had one somewhere. Looky."

"Which one? They all look alike."

"This is my brother here on the left. That's Cousin Pierre next, and here, the last one, sort of behind the jasmine bush is——"

"Flora, you are the craziest thing. He *is* behind the jasmine bush!"

"But you can see——"

"Nothing at all. *You* can because you know what he looks like."

"Oh," Flora peered closely. "He *is* kind of dim, isn't he?"

"Tell me about him, instead."

"He's handsome."

"That all?"

"Dark brown, like me. Quick—quick-tempered, too. You ought to see him sometimes. Well—he looks like all the Grandolets," she concluded simply.

"Wonderful! I have a perfect picture of him."

"You're making fun of me again. He's rich."

"Is that a Grandolet characteristic, too?"

"Pretty near. Most of 'em have *lots* of money. But these Grandolets haven't close kin. Niles is almost alone. His father and mother are dead. His grandfather and his aunt live with him."

"Don't you mean he lives with *them?*"

"No. White Cloud belongs to Niles."

"Is that a place?"

"Yes. The old Grandolet place. Awful big, and ver-ry nice." The word "very" sometimes tripped Flora's French tongue. "It's the name of the house and the plantation, too. You get lost in that house, though, and I think it has ghosts in it."

[31]

"Nonsense! Why isn't your cousin married? I thought all of you married early down there."

"Mostly. But Niles is special. He is so easygoing. He is always making fun—carrying on like anything with everybody. But he is serious, too. Mama says he is a very wise manager."

"Has he had sweethearts?"

"Oh, many. He is a catch—and he is so nice, too."

"Twenty-six. Do you suppose he has had a lot of affairs?"

"Oh, Victoria!" Flora's tone retreated from its frank enthusiasm. "How—oh, I don't know."

"Don't be silly, Flora. I notice that all of you know everything about each other. I just wondered what a young man as fascinating as you say he is——"

"Oh, well—I suppose—I have heard little stories now and then, but we don't talk about such things."

"Why not?" Victoria was curiously persistent.

"Well, in the first place, there would be the kind of girls —not nice—girls we don't know, and—and all that."

"I've read about New Orleans and those exotic—what do you call them—octoroons?"

Flora froze. "That must have been in the old days. I don't know anything about such things."

Victoria's look was cryptic. "I somehow imagine your Louisiana men to be—well, quite hotheaded and impulsive."

"Oh, yes, in many ways. Now, Niles—when he sees the girl, or—or makes up his mind—zing!" Flora snapped her fingers. "It will be like that."

The ten days of final examinations and commencement events were mixed at Fairfield into an unbelievable melee of hysteria and gleeful release.

"It's like judgment day!" Flora declared—highly uncertain

of the outcome of mathematics tests. But Flora's excitement about her brother and Niles prevailed and the contagion spread to her immediate acquaintances. When Louis Vélazy and Niles Grandolet arrived they were subjected to a flutter of attention that bewildered them a little.

Louis Vélazy was like Flora. Niles Grandolet was something else. Victoria realized that Flora had not adequately described him. She also realized that there was something more than cousinly interest there—something on the tremulous verge of becoming a sudden emotional crisis. These Southerners!

Niles Grandolet was not very tall. He was quick of motion as Flora had said. The first thing that Victoria noticed was the fascinating way his eyes and hands began to talk before he said a word, and how they continued to make amusing comments and amendments after he had finished speaking. He was handsome—yes—but not too much so. He had the grace and the complete ease of the typical "nice" Southerner. He looked French or Spanish, or something unfamiliar, she thought. He also had the somewhat annoying air of insolence and easy superiority she had come to associate with the few men of the far South she had met.

The first time they were left alone Niles moved closer to Victoria.

"Flora didn't tell me," he said plaintively.

"Didn't tell you what?" Victoria's question was honest.

"That you are probably the most beautiful girl in the world."

"Oh." Victoria made the single word sound flat, chilling, and faintly edged with distaste. But Niles Grandolet was not the kind of person who accepted such nonsense from girls. He did not even guess that she intended each separate shade of meaning. He looked her up and down with a single flash of his eyes.

The week was crowded with teas, class receptions, art exhibits, recitals, ivy plantings, and the like. Unexpectedly Niles Grandolet did not win great favor with the girls. Twenty-six or twenty-seven was rather old for their interests. Willie Lou Rogers pretended to have observed several gray streaks in Niles' blue-black hair. Flora exploded like fireworks. Anyway, she concluded, the Grandolets were all prematurely gray. Flora's brother, Louis, with his dancing eyes and dancing feet was an unequivocal success.

Flora managed to throw Victoria and Niles together as much as possible. She was terribly afraid Niles might suspect that he was regarded as belonging almost to an older generation. But always when she saw him the look in her eyes deepened. Victoria was observant. Was the look tenderness, or question, or just watchful concern? She could not say.

Niles had a gaily familiar way with Flora. Once when she kissed him good night her lips lingered a little and she dug her sharp little nails suddenly into his arms. He seemed not to notice but she swayed dizzily toward him. He broke the spell instantly with a quick laughing remark and said a hurried good night.

The next evening Miss Harper and Miss Haynes gave their usual party for the seniors. Victoria and Niles were together most of the evening. Flora was feverishly active, lending a sprightly assistance everywhere and doing much to lessen the stiffness of this half-dreaded event. She appeared not to see either Victoria or Niles, but both of them were oddly aware of her.

"Victoria," Niles spoke softly. His face was serious.

"Yes?"

"There was something else Flora didn't tell me."

"What is that?"

"That I'd probably fall in love with you—zing!" He snapped his fingers. "Just like that."

The repetition of Flora's phrase and gesture made her laugh. Niles touched her arm. "Let's go outside. It's hot in here."

Outside he made straight for a sheltered corner of the terrace. There was a large Chinese lantern over a wrought-iron bench. Niles reached up and put out the light.

He sat close to her and laid his arm along the back of the seat.

"Now! How old are you?"

Victoria stiffened. "Well——"

"Oh, I remember now. Flora told me. You are twenty. It didn't seem important—then. You're from New Hampshire. It must be a terrible place to live, but of course you won't have to do that any more. Your father is rector of a church. That's nice. We're Protestant, too—ever since my grandfather married a Niles. Before that we were Catholic. Really—you are prettier than I thought you were ten minutes ago."

"That's——"

"The moonlight? No. Moonlight doesn't fool me. I'm used to it. You ought to see our Louisiana moon. But you will. Flora says you speak pretty good French. That's nice, too. My grandfather likes to speak French. I can't much—just never did, somehow. All the old ways are changing down there. You haven't any brothers and sisters and you think you are going to teach school. You'd become White Cloud—that's home, you know. All the White Cloud women have been beautiful. Now —let's see—what do you want to know about me?"

"Not anything, really——"

"Then Flora told you far more than I suspected."

"You think poorly of yourself, don't you?"

"No. The Grandolets——"

"Yes, yes, I know. Suppose we go in."

"Not yet. I've a lot more to say." He laid his hand on hers and left it there for a moment, then abruptly he drew her to him and kissed her on the mouth. Under the fervor of that kiss Victoria remained impassive. Niles felt her lithe, sweet roundness in his arms, soft but not yielding. There was something unawakened, virginal, untried in her lack of response. A tingle of satisfaction swept through him. This was right, this was as it should be. It was according to the code he knew. Women should never show passion—certainly not before marriage—perhaps not ever. He had often heard the question discussed. For one uncomfortable, fleeting instant, he thought of Flora.

That night as she was undressing, Victoria turned from the mirror. "Flora, tell me something about White Cloud."

Flora looked suddenly a little haggard. Her lower lip trembled slightly and she pressed the back of her hand against her mouth for a moment before answering.

"Well——"

Victoria listened carefully this time. She saw the beginning of havoc in Flora's childlike face, but she rejected the inclination of her heart. A thousand scattered fragments of old thoughts, of doubts, and wonder, of worry and indecision swept magically together—to a center of clear design, to a resolve at once fixed and hard.

Flora talked on, watching Victoria with anxious eyes. Gradually her own mobile little face set. The flowerlike youth went out of it. A look came over her features that was at once strange and curiously suitable, as if underneath her lighthearted mask this had been long in preparation, long in waiting. Now it was indeed another face, an older one, eloquent of her own quixotic generosity, her selflessness. The new expression held without a tremor, sustained by the full strength of twenty generations of breeding and good manners.

She lifted her head slightly, and crossed the room. She touched Victoria's shining hair. "I couldn't think of a nicer cousin than you," she said softly.

"Don't be silly, Flora." Victoria spoke almost harshly. She was annoyed and disconcerted that Flora should have read her so perfectly.

"I'm not silly, Victoria. I guess I never was less silly in my whole life."

Victoria and Niles Grandolet were to be married two days after school closed, in the private parlor of Miss Harper and Miss Haynes.

Dr. Dunstan came from New Hampshire at Victoria's urgent insistence. He could not well afford the journey but he did not mention that.

Victoria met him at the school station. He kissed her on both cheeks. "My dear Victoria."

"Let's send your bag up by the school bus. Do you mind walking? I must talk to you."

"Why, of course. There's nothing troubling you—you are happy, aren't you?"

"Certainly. Only, I think you and I must be agreed on certain things. I suppose you think I am making a hasty and maybe an unconsidered marriage. I'm not too impulsive. I think you know that."

Dr. Dunstan listened, his head tilted a little to one side. He nodded at her last phrase, and a half-wry smile came to his lips. "I think you can be safely exonerated of that charge," he said quietly.

Victoria frowned. This tone of voice from her father had always disconcerted her, and she did not like to be disconcerted. She was silent for a few moments.

"What things, Victoria—what things do we have to agree on?"

She linked her arm in his and held his hand, palm to palm, as she used to do when she was a little girl. She saw that he was pleased at the old affectionate gesture.

As she talked, Dr. Dunstan's face changed. His look became more and more troubled.

"Victoria, my dear, I—I'm not so sure. It doesn't seem wise to begin your life this way."

"I didn't begin my life—others began it for me."

"Yes, yes, I know. But your husband—his family—it's a kind of deceit."

"Isn't it what I have heard you call a benevolent deceit?"

"I don't think——"

"Anyway, it is really no more of a deceit than we have practiced all these years—on everybody."

"But—I told *you.*"

"Yes—the one person who could best have done without that knowledge."

"Are you blaming me, Victoria?"

"No. I—I am obliged to you for your care."

"That's scarcely the word that I'd like to hear from you. But suppose later—much later—the truth should become known?"

"How could it?" She asked the question sharply.

"I don't know. I don't know. Only—I feel deeply the necessity for truth at all times."

"What truth do we know—either you or I? Only that I know nothing about myself!"

"Yes, yes. But still——"

"Listen, Father. This is my marriage. The decision as to how it is going to be is entirely my own. I prefer to—to keep my secret."

Later Dr. Dunstan had talked with her again.

"I like this young Mr. Grandolet, dear. He is a very fine person. High principles and—so much that I have hoped for you."

"I am glad that you do like him. Now you understand my wishes, don't you?"

"Less than ever. Niles is very much in love with you. I feel that a frank revelation would only deepen his affection and —and his sympathy."

"I don't want his sympathy. I'm afraid you don't understand these Southerners. They are horribly proud."

"Well," Dr. Dunstan sighed, "I can only say, my child, that I am a little sad of heart about this, and deeply uneasy."

A look of quick alarm flashed over her face. "Why? Is there anything important you have kept from me?"

"No, Victoria, nothing."

Victoria grasped his arm with an impatient gesture. "Please try to understand. Niles chose me for myself. As Victoria Dunstan I am all right. From here on I must go alone. I must make my way among—well, I don't know what difficulties. I mustn't be handicapped. I *mustn't*. As Victoria Grandolet I shall be safe."

And now in this failing light, not unlike the failing light of that other day, she was saying to herself again: "Safe. As Victoria Grandolet I am safe. Quite safe."

The subtropic twilight dropped quickly, and she went slowly across the lawn and into the house.

She closed the door of her room and stood there considering it. This was her room, her husband was here in this house, this house was her home. She would live here like all of the Grandolet women before her. She would have children here, she would doubtless die here—all of life that was to be hers would be lived here. But still she felt herself an alien to its habits and history, even to its physical surroundings. She was no real part of the house, nor of the life in it.

She could hear Aunt Lucie's words again, recited as if they were fragments of a familiar and accepted creed—*Niles was born in that room—in that bed; and his father and his grandfather.*

She stood looking at the monumental bed set on a dais, two steps from the floor. A huge canopy reached nearly to the ceiling. The four posts were shaped like classic columns, but instead of a conventional capital they were surmounted with a ring of carved camellias. This bed, not unlike others in the house, was hardly an article of furniture. It was an architectural feature, solid, immovable.

. . . his father and his grandfather.

This bed—this particular bed in the Grandolet house was a kind of family altar. One was conceived there, one was born there, one died there.

White Cloud. She lifted her head and looked at herself in the mirror. She was startled by a quick rush of feeling. White Cloud! She realized all at once that she wished to be a part of it, that she was suddenly and fiercely possessive of it. But suppose White Cloud did not want her!

She recalled a phrase Niles had used at Fairfield—a phrase she had not understood: "You will become White Cloud."

She had heard the colloquialism several times since. Just once when she had worn a particularly pretty dress, Aunt Lucie said, "My dear, you become White Cloud." She smiled now at the quaintness of the words. *Was* she becoming to it? She wished to be. She *must be*.

Once Orlou had said, "White Cloud won't take what it don't like. No matter who it is, if this house don't like somebody, it won't take him in. It'll destroy him first."

She had laughed. "Nonsense, Orlou. White Cloud is after all just a house."

"No, Miss Victoria, it's more'n a house. What ain't proper to it, it won't have. I've seen it lots of times. Didn't you notice already some people ain't easy here? Mr. Julien says it's a noble house and you got to be noble to live in it."

"That might be true, Orlou. It *is* a beautiful house."

"Somethin' more to it than that, though. It likes you or it don't."

Victoria had been amused at the time. It was the kind of picturesque nonsense that belonged to an old place with a colorful past. Later she thought of the matter again, more gravely. Yes; a house, a place, created out of the combined personalities of many individualistic people, representative of them, expressive of them—such a house might come to be a kind of projection of them all and so make its unfailing impression on others. A slight creepiness tingled at the back of her neck. She laughed to herself. "I'm getting to be like everybody else here; making up ghosts and then being scared by them." She said that over again to herself and felt a curious and not easily defined pleasure in the thought.

She found herself musing more and more on the past. The house itself, built slowly by black slaves, the gradual accumulation of its treasures from other houses, from the East, from Europe; the extravagant, thoughtless society of the river country, the shadow of the war, the Federal gunboats passing out there on their way to the siege of Vicksburg—one could have stood here at these windows and have seen them pass—and then the tragic collapse of everything that had made White Cloud and places like it. She caught herself with surprise that she—a Northerner—was thinking of the Southern defeat as a tragedy.

The house must have been silent and desolate during those years after the fall of the Confederacy. The families scattered, the laughter silenced, and the gaiety gone forever. But the Grandolets came back—to a changed world, yes, but they had come back. Now she was one of them. She had not exactly felt like this before. Again she sensed the oppression of all this long past in which she had no part—a past which was so stubbornly alive in the present. The technique of understanding it and using it as a method of living was incredibly difficult. She thought of Flora. Flora would have understood everything.

This room—it was terribly silent. She would have been glad of a ghost.

Victoria held her hands to her temples. She arose and walked back and forth. She thought again of those other times when she had been troubled. Those troubles had been abstractions, too. They might have done infinite damage had she not seen that she must use them and not be used *by* them.

She stopped and sat down again, thinking fast. *Use them.* That was it . . . White Cloud—its past and its people might indeed be strange and curious forces, but they were accountable, too, they were calculable.

. . . *All of the mistresses of White Cloud have occupied these rooms* . . .

Niles came in through the bedroom. "Hello, Vicky. Dreaming?"

"Just thinking."

[42]

He took off his coat. "Oh, by the way, I had a letter from Flora."

"Really? What did she say?"

"Said they were not going to Ponchartrain this summer. She and the family are going to Europe—already gone by this time, I guess."

"I wonder why she didn't write to me."

"Don't know, honey, couldn't say. We've always written to each other a lot."

Niles sat rubbing the back of his head.

"What's the matter, Niles?"

"With me? Oh, nothing."

"You look troubled—a little."

"Just plantation stuff, I suppose. I—I was thinking about Ponchartrain. Maybe you should go over to the summer place and leave me here for a while. There are a few things I've just got to look after this year, and it's getting pretty hot. Do you mind the heat much, honey?"

She made a half-humorous grimace. "I'm not used to it, yet."

"I know, I know. Well, what do you say you and Aunt Lucie——"

"No, Niles. I wouldn't want to go without you."

He looked pleased, and a deeper color showed in his sun-burned face. "Honest, Vicky? Honest?"

"Of course."

He arose and drew her close. "Sometimes I've thought——"

She waited a moment and then she said reluctantly, "You thought what?"

"That maybe you didn't care much about me."

"Oh, Niles!"

"I mean it. We've been married more than a month, Victoria."

"Well——"

"And—oh, I don't know how to say it to you." He held her tighter and kissed her hard on the mouth. She drew away a little.

"There! That's what I mean, Vicky. You're pretty darned unresponsive."

"Let's don't talk about it, Niles, please." She placed her hands against his chest. A quick flush darkened his face.

"Well, doggone it, we're married, aren't we?"

She did not answer. Her eyes looked past him. His flush deepened, and he stepped back.

"I guess if you'd think a little you might learn a few things."

"Niles, do we have to talk like this?"

Anger leaped up like a flame in his eyes. "Yes, *yes!*" He almost shouted the words.

She sat down in front of her dressing table. "I don't think so," she said quietly.

He tried to laugh. "You'd better think so."

"Why?"

Niles answered with a deliberate nonchalance. "I can't recall that any of the Grandolets were ever very patient men."

"Is that why I see so many children around the countryside who look like Grandolets?"

An instant fright drenched her with cold. Niles' face went blank.

"I wouldn't ever say that again if I were you, not ever, do you hear?" His voice was low and level. "You'd better get ready to go to Ponchartrain next week."

Victoria watched him leave the room. Then she turned to her table and reached for her brush and comb. The gesture froze as she looked in the mirror. Orlou was standing motionless in the next room.

[44]

THREE

VICTORIA OPENED HER EYES. The morning sun coming through carefully adjusted shutters filled the room with a soft aqueous light. Its cool look was deceptive. A wave of drowsiness swept over her and she closed her eyes again. The sheltered silence of the great room came instantly alive with a multitude of small sounds. Birds in the high trees about the house, Negro voices from the distant kitchen court, the faraway crack of a whip and the creak of a wagon. Then there was the soundless, vibrant quality of the house, compounded maybe of the stir of air, the indistinguishable passage of people in another wing, but conveying always the sense of being itself alive and participant.

The first moments of waking were for Victoria moments of intense awareness and of almost poignant sensation. She was still strange enough to the place to feel each morning the bewilderment of its unfamiliarity. She sat up and looked about her. She must have slept very soundly. She had not known when Niles left for his early-morning tour of the plantation.

Sinking back into the pillows and stretching herself straight she brought her scattered thoughts briskly to attention. There were some things she must think about. She must marshal them, set them in sequence, and think them through. If ever she was to organize her own world of White Cloud and place it to her purposes, it must be now.

White Cloud—an agreeable appreciation of her own firmness and the order of her impressions cleared her thought—White Cloud was a formidable constellation of forces. A family molded into a pattern of purposeful design and direction, a tradition distilled from endless preferences and refusals, and a house which was a precise projection of these qualities. Individuals were born into the immediate range of this flux of powers and had little choice but to accept. Victoria had already heard Aunt Lucie speak of relatives who "did not seem to belong to us, somehow."

Other individuals married into this same intricacy. Victoria gathered that the Grandolet women learned the difficult code, became satellites of the system, and merged indistinguishably into its operation. The measure of one's success was the degree to which one became a real Grandolet. Aunt Lucie explained that her own mother understood the place and the family so well that she finally came to be like a born Grandolet.

Victoria had looked quizzically at Aunt Lucie.

"It seems an oddly oblique appreciation of your mother, Aunt Lucie."

"Oh, Victoria, you use such strange words! I don't always understand what you mean. I'm such a simple person. My mother was Isabella Niles, of course."

"What do you mean by 'of course'?"

"I think you are teasing me, Victoria."

"It seemed to me you were saying that being a Niles wasn't as good as being a Grandolet."

"Oh, my goodness, no! How could you think of such a thing? Being a Grandolet is just different, that's all."

"So——"

"So when I say she got to be like a born Grandolet, I—I guess I mean to show how successful she was."

"Oh!"

"That's all, Victoria. But never mind, dear, you'll come to understand us. There's nothing difficult about us, really."

After a moment Aunt Lucie added, irrelevantly, "Wyandotte belonged to old Judge Chetsworth Niles."

"What is Wyandotte, Aunt Lucie?" she asked patiently.

"Oh, my dear, don't you know? Wyandotte is the next big plantation south of White Cloud. It is a very fine place, but of course the house isn't anything like this one."

"Whose is it, yours?"

"No, no. It belongs to—to Flora."

Victoria had noticed the tiny hesitation in Aunt Lucie's sentence.

"Flora's? Really? I don't believe she ever told me about it."

"Well, you see, Flora's people have lived in New Orleans for a long time. The house has been closed for years. Niles runs the plantation. Flora inherited it from Aunt Carrie Niles."

"Why, I thought Flora was related on the Grandolet side."

"Both sides. But very distant. You must have Niles show you the place. The gardens are very good."

The conversation that day had drifted off into a hopelessly confusing saga of family connections. Victoria smiled at the recollection.

She knew she had won Aunt Lucie—at least temporarily, when she declined to assume the direction of the house. "I should make too many mistakes. You know I lived in a tiny rectory with only one maid—I have no experience or training for this. You must teach me. Anyway," she added, "you *look* like the chatelaine of this house."

Aunt Lucie was pleased to the bone. White Cloud was the dear possession of her soul.

Victoria swung herself out of the high bed. "O-oh, it's hot," she said to herself. She opened a shutter. Two great mimosa trees, one yellow, the other pink, stood near the semicircular gallery. The clusters of silky blossoms filled the air with their spicy perfume, but it was a perfume that was already linked in Victoria's mind with the simmering heat. Not a feathery leaf of the mimosas stirred. The white blaze of sunlight was like a conflagration.

"It *is* hot," she repeated.

"Yes'm." Orlou's voice from the door startled her. Orlou always came and went like a shadow. "Good morning, ma'am."

"Good morning, Orlou."

"Here's your coffee." She proffered a small cup of hot, black coffee. "Your breakfast will be here in a minute."

"What time is it?"

"'Bout ten, I guess. You must have slept good."

"I did. Has Mr. Niles come in yet?"

"No'm. He said he'd be gone awhile. He was going 'way down to the Far Félice swamp."

Victoria made a face at the strong coffee. "Where is that, Orlou?"

"Far Félice? It's the upper plantation."

"Goodness, I guess I'll be a long time learning this geography."

"Yes'm. Far Félice is just the next plantation up the river. Don't nobody live there now. The house is all going to rack and ruin, too."

"Why?"

"Nobody ever wanted to live there, I guess, after the war."

"Oh, my. You're going to be mysterious, aren't you, Orlou?"

"No'm. Just nobody wants to live there."

"Whose place is it?"

"Ours."

"What?"

"It was always a Grandolet place, but after White Cloud was finished Far Félice was just shut up."

"Did—did anything happen there?"

Orlou's heavy eyes drooped a little. "They used to say——"

"*Who* said?"

A quick little rap at the door interrupted. "It's me, Victoria. Are you up?"

"Oh, Aunt Lucie! Yes, come in."

Orlou held out a lacy negligee. "Quick, Miss Victoria, get into this. You look pretty near naked in that nightgown you got on."

Victoria smothered her laugh, but she was pleased at this proprietary sentence. It marked a change in Orlou.

Aunt Lucie crossed to the window and kissed Victoria on the cheek.

"I'm lazy this morning, Aunt Lucie."

"Goodness me, what else could anybody be in such weather?"

"Niles said last night he thought we should go to Ponchartrain right away."

Aunt Lucie looked a little troubled. "I hate to go."

"Why?"

"Well, Niles has to attend to some things here, and I hate to leave him."

"Of course. I told him yesterday that I didn't want to go without him."

"Naturally, but we haven't spent a summer here for years. It's terrible."

"Why does Niles have to stay on this year?"

"Well, I don't exactly know. I never understood business affairs of the place too well. He just talks things over with his grandfather."

"Yes, I know, but——"

"Maybe we're short of money this year. I heard him saying something about selling some timber from Far Félice."

Victoria looked surprised. Aunt Lucie noticed the look, and went on rather slowly, as if she were selecting words with care.

"We're not really rich in money, you know, Victoria."

"No, Aunt Lucie, I didn't know."

Aunt Lucie gazed at Victoria very straight. "Did you think we were, dear?"

"I didn't think anything about it one way or the other. I knew nothing about the Grandolets or White Cloud, except stray things Flora told me."

"Well, it's like this. There's lots and lots of land. Sometimes we're—well, I guess you'd say well off, other times we're short of actual money. Not that we exactly have to have it. This is a different kind of life from any you know, I suppose."

Victoria nodded. She was aware that both Aunt Lucie and Orlou were watching her.

"Orlou, where's Miss Victoria's breakfast?" For a moment Aunt Lucie seemed embarrassed. Her eyes wandered a little.

"It's coming, Miss Lucie."

"Well, as I was saying—now, what *was* I saying? Oh, yes— now, Flora is situated quite differently." Her bright eyes were steady again. "Flora is quite rich."

"I—I think I knew that."

"The Vélazy fortunes were in a way part of the Grandolet properties. From time to time during the past hundred years or so, these family fortunes were reunited by marriage. It seemed wise at the time, I dare say."

"A bit feudal, wasn't it?"

"What? Oh, yes, I suppose it seems so." A faint flush arose in Aunt Lucie's face. Victoria wondered if this conversation was accidental or not. Was she being told that White Cloud would have fared better with Flora and Flora's money? A slight shiver ran over her. Here was a signal—one of the first fragments of guidance she had received here.

Aunt Lucie apparently sensed the dangerous ground. She went on rather airily. "You must talk to Niles about the place and his work. His heart is wrapped up in it. Here's Luther with your breakfast."

"I think I'll have it out on the gallery. Will you have some coffee with me?"

"No, no, dear. I must run on in a minute. It's pretty hot out there, I expect. Niles seems to be late getting back. I declare, Victoria, I don't believe he's had breakfast downstairs a single time since you came."

"Orlou said he'd gone to Far Félice this morning. I wish you'd tell me something about Far Félice. Orlou was so mysterious I couldn't get anything out of her."

Victoria saw a quick glance exchanged between the two. Warning from Aunt Lucie, she was sure.

"Niles will take you up there some time."

Victoria lingered over her breakfast. Orlou stood back of her, near the high wrought-iron balustrade. Victoria had become somewhat more accustomed to the strange hovering presence of her maid. Orlou seemed always to be near, just around the corner, or in the next room. She did not actually anticipate needs; she seemed rather to create them, to establish a routine herself which enclosed Victoria in a sort of transparent protection. Just lately, Victoria had felt a slight comfort in the woman's watchful companionship. It was like having a wall at one's back.

Victoria shaded her eyes and looked out toward the river. Heat waves danced along the levee, breaking the shapes of trees and branches into a wavering unreality. The river was almost lost in a dreamlike haze, but the majesty of its great curve gave back to the entire landscape a strange grandeur. It was as if the river itself were a mighty actor in the ancient drama of this land.

She tried hard to see through the obscuring heat. After a moment the motion of the water became apparent. The powerful sweep, unhurried and irresistible, was like visible time. Wait, it seemed to say, presently I shall bring great events—curious, unguessed, and fateful.

Yes, she thought in answer to her fancy, I shall be here to see them. There is something important about all of this. There is nothing trivial here. The place, and time in this place, have stature. One must have stature to remain.

All that she had heard of local history and the little that she had read impressed her. It is a dark land, she thought. Its past seems dark, too, and bloody. Maybe the dramatic magnificence of landscape—of sky and sinister black land under it—begets events of drama.

Aunt Lucie, now—well, Aunt Lucie could talk all she liked about the Grandolets being simple people. "Just country people," she was fond of saying. Niles often echoed the words. But those words were not true. Outwardly everything seemed obviously just what it appeared to be—the easy tempo of life, the ambling Negroes, the straggle of outbuildings and quarters beyond the hedges enclosing the gardens, the common-place talk of planting, of crops and markets—but all of this was like a shabby and worn scabbard encasing a lithe blade of Damascus steel. The soul of White Cloud, and Victoria knew now that it had a soul, was not simple, might not even be benevolent.

"Mr. Niles is coming." Orlou spoke very quietly. She intoned the words as if they were part of a ritual.

Victoria came abruptly out of her reverie.

"Where? How do you know, Orlou?"

"I heard his horse, 'way off." She turned her head. "I hear him now. Can't you?"

"No."

Orlou went into the house and returned with a mirror and a powder puff. "Better fix your face a little, ma'am, you're kind of damp. It's mighty hot."

Presently Victoria saw Niles coming down the levee road. He left his horse at the hedge and walked across the garden. He stopped to look at something in a pool. He carried his hat in his hand, and his rather longish hair turned back from his brow in a Byronic wave. He was deeply sunburnt.

Victoria watched his easy, almost velvety walk, the high carriage of his head, the spirited, casual, but impatient and arrogant look of the whole man. He looks like a glorified faun, she thought.

He saw her and waved. " 'Lo, Vicky."

She raised her arm high and straight, and he waved again.

She heard him taking the central stairs, apparently three at a time, and the soft thump of his quick step. He came through the window, banging the French shutter out of his way.

He kissed her lightly on top of her head.

"Breakfast?" she asked.

"I had something at Tom Ward's before I went to the swamp."

"Terribly hot down there?"

"Just like a wet hell."

"Better have something, Niles."

"All right."

"Orlou."

"Yes'm."

"Tell Luther to bring Mr. Niles another breakfast. A pitcher of cool lemonade, too."

"Yes, ma'am."

Niles looked at her with a curious expression. He half smiled. It was the first time Victoria had ever given an order in the house. She realized instantly the import of his look. She could see that he was amused, and pleased.

"Niles."

"Yes, darling?"

"Aunt Lucie doesn't wish to go to Ponchartrain."

"Did she say so?"

"Yes."

"Why?"

"Wants to look after you."

"Nonsense. House full of servants."

"I don't wish to go, either."

He stared. "But why?"

"You have to stay, don't you?"

"Yes, I guess so."

"You can tell me why some other time. But if you stay here, I will, too."

"But why, Vicky?"

"Will you believe me if I tell you?"

"Of course. What's happening around here?"

"Nothing strange, Niles——"

"But see here, Vicky, everybody in the parish has gone on to the summer places. That's why you haven't met anybody yet. Some of 'em down on the coast, but a lot of our friends are at the lake. I'd like 'em to——"

"That can wait until fall, can't it?"

"Well——"

"Listen, Niles." Victoria looked out toward the garden.

"Yes, honey."

"I want to have a baby." The words were muffled and scarcely audible.

Niles flushed darkly, and swallowed hard. "Well——"

She smiled, though her color mounted. "There's no sign yet——"

Niles leaned back in his chair and roared. "So you think you'd better stay on and let's work at it, eh?"

"Oh, Niles!"

"It's magnificent."

"Sh! Orlou."

Orlou came with fresh coffee. "Mr. Niles' breakfast wili be right here, Miss Victoria, in just a minute."

Niles winked at Victoria.

Victoria went back to her imperturbable dignity.

"But I wonder, Niles——" she bit her lip thoughtfully.

"Wonder what?"

"Maybe Aunt Lucie should go. I could look after you. And perhaps Grandfather Julien should go."

"Oh, Lord, he never felt better in his life. He is just like an old palmetto, rattles in the heat and likes it. And as for Aunt Lucie, she'd prefer to stay here if hell shut in around us."

"Then——"

"Later on the mosquitoes——"

Orlou shifted the plates on the table. "Lots of mosquitoes at Ponchartrain, too, Mr. Niles."

Niles grinned at her. "Want to stay on here, too, eh?"

"I like it here."

"Well, looks like——"

"Niles, what kind of house have you at the lake?"

"*We,* you mean. Big, sprawly, one story, shuttered porches— Mediterranean kind of house. Painted pink."

"It sounds charming, but I don't want to go—yet."

"We'll see. Maybe later on."

"Now, Niles, I want to know about Far Félice."

His face darkened suddenly.

"Here's yo' breakfus', Mr. Niles."

"Oh, hello there, Luther."

"I brung you some col' ham and some devil' eggs, and some——"

"That's fine. That's fine. Now——"

"I bet hit's hot down in 'at swamp."

"Sitting on top of hell, Luther."

"Sho is glad I don' have to be down 'ere." Luther, black and dry and gay, departed.

"Poor devil." Niles looked after him through half-closed lids. "He thinks hanging over a cookstove is heaven."

"About Far Félice——"

"It's just a plantation. Deserted house."

"Why?"

"Old one. Part of it burned down away back—oh, I guess around 1830, earlier maybe."

"Grandolets lived there?"

"Yes. I don't know all about it, Victoria, but old Quintin Grandolet, my great-grandfather, died there."

"Oh."

"He was killed."

"How?"

"Well, Victoria, I suppose you may as well hear about it. It's an ugly story. There was a violent family quarrel. Somehow—no one, of course, ever knew the details—somehow two Grandolets were killed."

Victoria leaned forward in her chair. "Do you mean they killed each other?"

"Yes."

"How, Niles?"

"Let's don't talk about it." He fidgeted in his chair and his deepened color stayed. "I don't even like to think about it."

She waited for a moment. "Did anyone know why they did it?"

"Yes, I guess so—after a while. At first it was thought they might have been killed by slaves. The library in which the murders occurred caught fire and that wing of the house was burned. Later on it came out, somehow, how and why it happened. And then it was sort of hushed up. We don't talk about it."

Victoria looked sideways at him and waited. "You haven't said what it was about."

He sighed impatiently. "I don't know why you're curious about it, but—they fought about a woman."

"Oh!"

"About Great-grandfather Quintin's wife."

"Niles, who was the other Grandolet?"

"Quintin's brother, Paul."

She nodded slowly. "Not surprising you didn't want to talk about it. Terrible, wasn't it?"

"They were a hotheaded lot in those days, I guess. All of

those Latins shot first and asked questions afterward. But Far Félice has been pretty much shunned. It's been thought of as a sort of bad-luck place."

"Then Grandfather Julien was born at Far Félice?"

"Yes. An uncle of his, Etienne Grandolet, finished White Cloud and brought Grandfather Julien here. Far Félice is actually in walking distance by the levee, but Grandfather has never been to the house. He's been to the cemetery, of course."

"What cemetery is that?"

"Our own."

"Oh." Victoria shivered a little. She suddenly thought of the Grandolet bed upstairs and Aunt Lucie's remark, "All of the Grandolets were born in that bed." She waited for the sentence she knew Niles was about to speak.

He spoke rather absently. "All of the Grandolets are buried there."

Victoria laughed shortly. It was no more than a hysterical catch in her throat, but Niles stared.

"I'm not laughing, Niles. You just startled me, that's all. You have everything here, haven't you, from the cradle to the grave?"

"Yes," he answered seriously. "I like it that way, Victoria. There's nothing macabre about it, I just like to feel that the whole cycle is lived out here where the others lived before me. I know where I'll be buried, exactly."

"Oh, Niles."

He laughed softly. "You, too."

"Please——"

"Oh, sorry. You'll get used to our familiarity with such matters. We're quite gay about the dead, sometimes. Sometimes we're superstitious as the Negroes themselves."

"As about Far Félice?"

"Well, I feel sort of queer about Far Félice. The place where things have happened makes you think about those things. There's an influence—maybe. Whatever you believe about it is so for you, I guess."

"Well, that was long ago——"

"Yes, but there are funny things down here. Old stories persist, old hates last, too."

"You don't mean——"

"I don't mean anything."

"Far Félice sounds frightening, somehow, the way you talk about it."

"No. It's spooky, though. The jungle has nearly taken it. Most Negroes won't go near it."

"Ghosts?"

"Hants is the word, darling. We don't have ghosts, or spooks. We have *hants*." He smiled again, and his usual lightness of manner returned.

"But you always have to be careful," he added thoughtfully.

"Of what?"

"Well, don't walk out of sight of the house alone. Not ever." He turned in his chair. "I have to see Grandfather Julien. Business, honey."

"You didn't tell me what you were doing at Far Félice."

"Timber."

"Yes?"

"Miles of swamps. Cypresses big as redwoods—well, almost! Sell 'em. Money, my darling Vicky, money. We can always use it."

"You're not in—in difficulties, are you?"

"Lord, no—no more than usual. We've got to learn some

things down here, though. We don't know anything but cotton and sugar. It's all too much for your spun-gold head, my sweetheart."

"I guess I could learn about it, couldn't I?"

"And when you had, what would you do about it?"

"You might get sick someday—or something."

"Listen. Old Tom Ward was born on White Cloud plantation. He knows more about it than all the Grandolet generations. We use a little of our own sense, but mostly we use his."

"He doesn't seem so old."

"He's sixty. But when he dies there'll be young Tom, or some one of his sons. They're White Cloud, too."

"And I—what do I do all my life? Really, Niles, I'm serious. I've been thinking."

"Along the right lines, too. Have a son to carry on, run White Cloud—it's a lot of house—just be you—that's enough. I've got to go along. See you after a while."

Victoria sat quietly. Orlou removed the dishes. Later she came out on the gallery two or three times, but Victoria was lost in her own thoughts.

Last night's few difficult moments had passed, leaving no trace of their passing. Niles doubtless had set it down to whim or temperament. These men were indulgent in some ways of their women, but Victoria sensed beneath this indulgence a kind of medieval stringency.

A child—yes, a son. That was important—and as quickly as possible. She was slightly embarrassed. It was silly, it was too obvious and simple, this frank and open use of the one power she possessed.

She was learning. She was learning rapidly, and her knowledge threw a retrospective revelation into surprising relief. She remembered that she had always been able to wheedle her father into doing anything she wanted. She had only to pet and caress and smother his refusals with childish kisses. Curious. Yes, very curious. An odd chilliness crawled slowly over her skin. She had never liked to be touched by anyone. She had always had to overcome an initial resistance whenever she set about winning the Reverend Dr. Dunstan over. Niles. Niles was a hot-blooded person. Would she—could she ever awake to respond, or would she have to hold tight to herself and—endure? She wondered, and as she wondered, she drew herself together in an attitude of cold distaste. She did not love Niles Grandolet. Whether she would ever love him, or even want to, was a consideration for the future.

FOUR

ORDINARILY VICTORIA ACCEPTED and wore whatever dresses Orlou laid out for her. This morning she was critical. She rejected a stiff-starched pique as unbecoming, another as too heavy for this hot day.

"That pale-green one, Orlou, with the embroidered polka dots."

"Yes'm. You'll need another petticoat, though. You don't want the sun shining right through you."

She shook her head, but Orlou was firm.

Orlou looked after her curiously as she left the room.

Victoria, too, considered herself with a new curiosity. Something had happened inside of her head this morning. She was different. Her step, as she rounded the gallery, felt light and assured. A quick excitement crowded her throat. Today—this day—every day was all at once charged with importance. They were her days, her own days "to do with," as Dr. Dunstan used to say.

She stopped for a moment to look at the long row of portraits that hung on this floor. Downstairs on the main floor there were a few, chosen perhaps for their decorative values. On the floor above were others, older and less important, she imagined, from a tribal point of view. She had never examined them very closely, although Aunt Lucie seldom passed without adding some detail to the many personal histories.

Victoria realized for the first time that she must know these long-vanished Grandolets. It was as important to know the dead Grandolets as it was to understand the living ones. These men and women, having no other visible presence than their portraits, were nevertheless a terribly vital part of today. They were the witnesses of the past and the secret, powerful index of the present. They were family.

As she thought of Grandfather Julien, of Aunt Lucie—yes, and of Flora—she knew that these old Grandolets, Vélazys, and Nileses were the direction, the counsel, the religion of the family's daily life.

She leaned close to read the tiny nameplates in the dim light. Delacour, Joinville, d'Aupais—Hippolyte d'Aupais, Santeuil, Gailhabaud, and the occasional English names, Harris, Seabrook, Cornwall. Two full-length paintings, flanking the entrance to Aunt Lucie's rooms, bore Spanish names. She could not quite make them out.

She made the round of the circle once more. These faces told her little. Bad painting, probably. The Grandolets looked much alike, most of them thin, bright-eyed, and supercilious—like Grandfather Julien. She looked for someone whom Niles might resemble. The smiling one—Hippolyte d'Aupais, maybe—a little. No, more than a little. As you looked at him his smile seemed to deepen. He had dimples, which Niles did not have, but the eyebrows slanted upward, and there was a mocking, go-to-hell look about him. But Victoria was more curious about the women. Niles' mother, Aunt Lucie's mother, Grandfather Julien's mother—those women who had slept and died in the great bed where, as Aunt Lucie had said, "Niles was born, and his father and his grandfather."

How had they lived? What had they thought? How had they met the challenge of White Cloud, and of Far Félice, and of that still earlier place which Niles said the river had taken long ago? She was of their company. She would learn little from Aunt Lucie, except of those attributes and actions which enhanced the Grandolet tradition. Maybe there were letters or diaries. But even these would likely tell nothing. These people kept their secrets. Each one met her own destiny in her own way. The roads they traveled, each ordained by a unique fate, were dim and far. People, she thought, were as lonely as planets, and as controlled by forces as impersonal and remote.

Niles' mother—"she was Gertrude Lacey from Tennessee," Aunt Lucie said—was young here in her rather ugly dress. She seemed out of place. She was too—too obvious a person. Victoria peered sharply at her. Was Gertrude Lacey a little overwhelmed by White Cloud and the Grandolets? The blurred, impassive face with all character painted out of it told her nothing at all. But Grandfather Julien's wife was different. Victoria made a sort of whimsical greeting to the grim portrait. Aunt Lucie's voice echoed again: "My mother was Isabella Niles, of course." *Of course.* Whatever it meant to be Isabella Niles, it was evident that Isabella Niles appreciated it. The painter had been unable to destroy *her.* A mere likeness sufficed to set her there, uncompromising, dominant, intelligent, arrogant, and cold.

Isabella Niles. Victoria decided she would find out more about her. She went downstairs.

Aunt Lucie was in the huge, stiff room which in early days had been the ballroom. She was surrounded by four or five maids and tall stacks of linen slipcovers.

"Now, let me see. Isn't there a label on those, Pinky?"

"No, ma'am."

"How careless. I suppose it fell off. But I think they belong in the library. Oh, hello, Victoria. This is so confusing. Every year it is the same. I store them away in order and they come out in confusion. Pinky, I think you and Emsy will just have to try them on until you find where they belong. I declare, I'll have to rest a little. Come along, Victoria; I think it's a bit cooler in that front corner room."

"Aunt Lucie, I was looking at the portraits upstairs."

"Yes? That's good. You may as well learn them. They're like the Shorter Catechism, or the Apostles' Creed, you have to know them sometime. The talk I've heard! But even now I believe Father knows more family history than I do."

"I was interested in one face especially."

"Who was it?"

"Hippolyte d'Aupais."

"Oh!" Aunt Lucie laughed. "Of course."

"Why? What's funny?"

"He looks like Niles—don't you think so?" Aunt Lucie's expression was a little sly.

"Y-es. I thought so."

"But Niles isn't like him. You must believe that."

"I don't know anything about him, Aunt Lucie."

"Of course, you don't. He was very bad."

"What did he do?"

"Wasted his life. Gambled—though I guess most everybody did back there. But"—Aunt Lucie leaned forward confidentially—"I guess you may as well know. He—he actually had two illegitimate children."

"Oh, my!" Victoria looked amused. "Didn't he marry the girl?" she asked mockingly.

"My dear, there were *two* girls—two girls of good families, too. His father sent him to Paris. They said—but I've only

[65]

heard it from quite unreliable sources—that he ran away from a duel. I'm not sure that I believe it."

Victoria kept a straight face. Aunt Lucie was very serious. "D'Aupais. How did he come into the family?"

"He was a Grandolet. D'Aupais was his middle name. His father forbade him the use of the family name."

"What became of him? I think he sounds interesting."

"He married an Italian girl. When his father died he came back. That's why Far Félice has an Italian name. He built it."

"Far Félice——"

"I should say it is Italian. We pronounce it French fashion, of course. Far Félice."

"I've been looking at the portrait of your mother, too. I think she's magnificent."

Aunt Lucie flushed with pleasure. "She was, Victoria. She *was* magnificent. During the war——"

But Victoria had heard this before. Her attention wandered. She was wondering what had become of Hippolyte d'Aupais' children.

Aunt Lucie's circuitous and intricate narrative went on and on. Pausing to interpolate extended lateral family histories, she continued to embroider with anecdote, and to bring back to shadowy life personalities which seemed to be as real as and sometimes more important to her than living relatives.

Victoria listened with half of her attention, considering from time to time this small room which she had never observed carefully before. It felt more intimate in character than anything she had experienced in the house. The walls were paneled, and the ceiling intricately molded. A slight and very slender chandelier hung from the elaborate central rosette. The mantel was surmounted by a square Venetian mirror, divided and subdivided into innumerable lozenges of yellowish glass.

The draperies and upholsteries were faded and worn, down-right shabby in places, but the room kept an air of tasteful elegance and of carefully guarded aloofness.

Aunt Lucie's chaotic stories sagged a little from their own weight. She seemed after a while to be talking softly to herself.

"This room, Aunt Lucie——"

"Yes, dear. What about it?"

"You tell *me* about it!"

The little old lady's cheeks glowed. Victoria realized how lonely Lucie Grandolet must have been all these years, how she must have lived for White Cloud, and how she must have made of it and its history the singular passion of her life. For just an instant Victoria felt an impulse of sympathy, but it was immediately chilled by something else—a feeling that Aunt Lucie Grandolet was after all only a temporary guardian of the special place held for the mistresses of White Cloud. Isabella Niles, then Gertrude Lacey from Tennessee, and now—Victoria Dunstan. A tiny rush of unreasoning resentment passed along her nerves. She came back abruptly to Aunt Lucie's words.

"—since after all there are mighty few places or corners in White Cloud that you could call exactly cozy. Mother chose it and furnished it for herself. She received intimate friends here, and sat here a great deal. Niles' mother never cared much for it, poor child——"

"Aunt Lucie! It's strange but I don't know about Niles' father and mother, except—let me see, I guess Flora told me—that they died young."

"It's incredible, my dear, but Niles never says anything about the family he doesn't have to, does he? His father—we always called him Jules, though he was named Julien—and Gertrude died in New Orleans of yellow fever."

"At the same time?"

"The same day. It was frightful. Yellow fever has been our terrible scourge, you know. They went there on a visit, expecting to stay just a few days, and——" Aunt Lucie wiped her eyes. "It was such a mercy they didn't take Niles with them. I took care of him myself—Orlou and I managed somehow."

"I'm sorry, Aunt Lucie. Don't talk about it if you don't want to."

"I'm glad to talk. There are many things you must learn about us. If you had grown up about here, it wouldn't be so difficult, would it? So many of the family, when I stop to think about it, Victoria, died so young. This is a violent country." She looked, unseeing, out of the window. "And we seem to have been a violent family, too," she added softly. "But I was telling you about this room. I never have used it much myself, though I guess you'd say it's understood it belongs to what Orlou calls 'the lady of the house.'"

She touched the heavy brocade of the draperies. "It's wonderful, isn't it, the way that has lasted? It's the original stuff. I suppose such things aren't made now. It's faded some, but I think I like it better that way. It kind of speaks of all the long years it has hung here, seeing all that happened, watching so many come and go. My mother's coffin stood here—right by this window. I remember it as if it were yesterday."

Victoria kept silent. Aunt Lucie had not talked like this before.

"My dear Victoria, why don't you adopt this room? You are the mistress of White Cloud now."

"I do like the big sitting room upstairs, Aunt Lucie. I like to see the river."

"I understand that so well, my child. The river is sort of company, isn't it? Before the levee was built you could see the river from these windows. I used to think when I was a young girl that I'd just die if I didn't have the river. It reminded me that there was a world outside, and people. That was right after the war and the whole country was like dead. We just waited. There'd be weeks and weeks when not a soul came to White Cloud. There were no young men. Those who weren't killed went off somewhere where they had some kind of chance. I guess—well, I guess that's why I never married. There just wasn't anybody."

Victoria felt that she should be touched. She knew Aunt Lucie was opening her heart, taking her, a stranger, into its intimate confidences, but she was unable to feel. It was too much like a story out of a book. It seemed to be too long ago and too far away to be more than just a story.

"Excuse me, Victoria. I don't know what's got into me, talking like this. But this room, now. I always feel that my mother's presence is here. All these little things, these knick-knacks, were hers. It was her place, and it should be yours by all rights."

"Oh, Aunt Lucie, I couldn't ever feel——"

"I know what you are going to say, but you are wrong. I have her stored away in my heart, but Isabella Niles became Isabella Grandolet and that part of her belongs to the family, just as you do now. Maybe, somehow, she'd give you something here. You might need it. Women don't have the easiest kind of time always, and—I guess I ought not to say so, but the Grandolet women sometimes have had a good deal to contend with. Not that I mean anything—goodness knows; Niles is a good boy—even if he does look like Hippolyte d'Aupais!"

Victoria laughed and Aunt Lucie smiled a bit wryly.

"I can't think that necessarily means anything, do you, Victoria?"

FIVE

As THE WEEKS PASSED, Victoria learned why a Louisiana summer was spoken of with dread. The heat increased steadily, implacably, each day more intense and more searing than the one before. The shutters throughout the house were carefully closed in the early morning, but despite the high ceilings and the wide spaces the air grew heavy and oppressive until by afternoon everyone was limp and listless. Niles grumbled, but he rode out a large part of the day. Aunt Lucie kept to her own rooms as much as possible, but Grandfather Julien took his morning walks in the garden, sometimes along the levee, and spent the rest of the day reading.

Victoria was restless. The days seemed interminable, and often the nights were torture. The thick mosquito canopies smothered every breath of air that might stir.

One morning she followed Grandfather Julien into the garden. He seemed fantastically thin, but he moved with an angular alacrity—like a marionette. He stopped and looked at her speculatively.

"It's hot for you to be out."

"It's hot inside, too."

"How are you making out with our Louisiana weather?"

She shrugged ever so slightly. "It's a new experience."

"Why don't you speak French to me?"

"*Si vous voulez——*"

"I think it would be appropriate if you said *tu.*"

Victoria looked up quickly in some surprise. "Do you mean it? I shall——"

"Of course. You are my grandson's wife. Now I'm going about the gardens. Do you wish to come along?"

She set her step with his. After a moment he pointed with his slender ivory-topped cane at a fancifully parterred corner. "Do you know any of these plants?"

She shook her head. "I don't believe I do."

"They're interesting. Many varieties. Unusual, some of them. I studied them once—the things in the swamps, too. Wanted to be a botanist, or something like that."

"Why didn't you?"

"Responsibilities. Other things to do."

"I can't imagine you not doing anything you wanted to."

"Why?"

"You look like you'd do what you wish—still."

"I'm seventy-two."

"I know."

He stopped and turned to look squarely at her. "Want some advice?"

She nodded.

"Learn something."

Victoria looked blankly at him.

The old man started forward. "Come on. We can talk as we go." They skirted the garden, keeping in the deeper shade of the dense hedges.

"I said learn something. I don't mean a hobby. I mean something that will be a refuge—a place of your own to live in."

"I'm not sure——"

"Let me talk. You don't look silly, though I don't know much about Yankee women."

"I was born in Canada, Grandfather Julien."

"Oh, were you? I didn't know."

"Father and Mother were English."

"Well, well, that's better. What I mean is this: you'll have to live here a long time. You can't be just an inhabitant of this big house. You have to do something about it, be somebody, master your life, or—or it will do something to you. That's all. Let's go in."

In the hall he walked toward the south wing. Without pausing or looking at her, he said rather self-consciously, "Want to come and read to me for a while?"

"I'll be glad to, of course."

They passed through the library and the breakfast room to the short open colonnade which connected the main house with the south wing. This wing was built in the detached manner of the older *garçonnières,* but was an extensive wing. Julien Grandolet occupied rooms at the front of this part of the house. Victoria had not been in them before. She looked about with interest. The furnishings were severe, but there were many books. The French windows looked out on a formally planned orangery.

"Sit down, sit down."

"Thank you, sir."

"Want to read French?"

"Whatever you'd like."

"Do you know Buffon?"

"By name."

"I'm going through him again. Here—let me see, yes, here we are. Do you know anything about books—editions, I mean?"

"Not much, I'm afraid. My father——"

"This is a first. Quarto, Paris, 1804. Look at those plates!"

"Um, beautiful, aren't they?"

"Very fine. Very interesting. Let's read—there, where I marked a page. Second paragraph."

Victoria moved her chair, and frowned. She was a bit nervous.

"All right, all right, begin. That's about *La Trachine vive*, most curious, most interesting."

She began slowly, enunciating as clearly as she could.

. . . Son nom fameux se lie à d'immortels souvenirs: mais à peine l'a t-on aperçu, que toute idée de grandeur s'évanouit: il ne lui reste plus que quelques rapports vagues avec la brillante chimère dont on lui a appliqué la fastueuse dénomination, et du volume gigantesque qu'on étoit porté a lui attribuer, il se trouve tout d'un coup réduit à des très petites dimensions. Ce dragon des mers, ou, pour mieux dire, et pour éviter toute cause d'erreur, la trachine vive ne parvient, en effet, très-souvent qu'à la longueur de trois ou quatre décimètres.

The old man chuckled. "Delightful, eh? Like many other histories of frightfulness—*ne parvient, en effet, qu'à longueur de trois ou quatre décimètres!*"

"But——"

"Yes?"

"Isn't Buffon, well, not very authoritative?"

"Who told you that?"

"I—I don't know for certain, but I seem to remember a natural-history teacher——"

"In that fool school you and Flora attended?"

She smiled gaily at him. "Yes."

"What of it?"

"Nothing, only——"

"Listen, my dear Victoria, I'm not going to school; I'm enjoying myself."

"Of course, of course."

"Do you suppose I care if that—what you have just read—is true or not?" He snapped his fingers. "I find it charming. I am seventy-two, and I like to read about birds and fishes and strange plants—it's all a kind of fairy story for old age. I demand only that it have order and design. It makes a house of fancy—maybe fact—for me to go about in. Do you understand?"

He took the book from her and flipped the page. "Look at the plate. Isn't our *Trachine vive* something for the fancy? Imagine him! Or"—the long brown fingers turned the pages rapidly—"look at this one—*Le Scorpine didactyle*. Figure that one to yourself! Is it not appropriate that he should swim in the mysterious waters of India? He is fabricated with imagination, that one!"

Victoria was astonished at the old man's vivacity. He seemed to have forgotten about the reading. He pointed out one strange monster after another. Evidently all of them were old acquaintances.

"It is a world, my child, a complete world. I can sit here in my chair and live in it. Often I have need to do so. You—you, too, must find such a world. If you have not the imagination you will not find it, but also in that case you will not need it, but if you have—aha! then you can never be made a prisoner of anything." He chuckled again, glanced at the page, and read softly: *Une beauté peu commune et une puissance dangereuse n'ont-elles pas toujours été les attributs distinctifs des enchanteresses créées par l'antique mythologie, ainsi que des fées auxquelles une poésie plus moderne a voulu donner le jour?*

He glanced quickly at her, his great brown eyes flashing

with malicious glee. "Don't tell me that Buffon is perhaps not scientific, nor even reliable. Is poetry true? Is poetry reliable? I say yes!"

Victoria nodded and reached for the book.

"No, no! You have nearly spoiled my pleasure in my fish for today. I admire reason, Victoria, but one must learn the right place for it. Unreason—what a happiness it can be!"

He blinked at her as one does at a child. "Now will you do as I say, and find something for yourself?"

"I already have a wish——"

"So? So? Would you like to tell me?"

"Yes, because you must help."

"Tell me."

"It's about White Cloud—the house, I mean."

"Yes, yes."

"I want to collect its story—complete——"

She hesitated. Julien leaned forward in his chair, his eyes were still and bright.

She went on uneasily. "There's something more than a house here—isn't there? I think I'd like to write it—maybe, when I'm older and understand better, to interpret it."

She waited for him to speak.

He shook his head a little. "I'm wondering about you."

"What? What are you wondering?"

"I am surprised that you sense—well, what there is here. So many people see only a big, fine house. There are other houses, finer ones, too, but you are right; this is more than a house. But——"

"You think I can't understand it because I'm what you called a 'Yankee woman' a while ago."

"I'll take it back. Isn't that what you say?"

"Right. I feel better."

"You'd find some black things, Victoria, but it is interesting. There are many letters and diaries here—we will see, we will see. Perhaps I may bring myself to talk, as well."

Victoria crossed the reception hall thoughtfully. She hesitated at the foot of the stairs, turned, and went back to Isabella Niles' room. She looked at it for a moment. There were two flower paintings on the wall, dark and out of keeping with the rest of the furnishings. Yes, they might come down. She closed the door and went upstairs. Aunt Lucie was coming down from the third floor.

"Oh, Aunt Lucie——"

"Where have you been, my child?"

"Reading to Grandfather."

"Really? How extraordinary!"

"Why?"

"Well, I don't know, he's just been so retiring for years."

"I enjoyed it. But—you gave me an idea one day. I've been thinking about it."

"What was that?"

"About Isabella Niles' room."

"Yes?"

"I think I *would* like to—to adopt it as you said."

"I think that's lovely. Now——"

"But there's something I'd like to change."

"Oh, my dear, what?"

"I'd like to have her portrait down there. It's in the dark up here. That's where she belongs."

Aunt Lucie seized Victoria's arm and squeezed it. "Victoria, you are going to be one of us! I can see it. I think it's a wonderful idea."

"May I do it, then?"

"Victoria, White Cloud is your house. Listen, why don't you take Hippolyte down, too? I think that would be nice."

Victoria colored a little. She had meant to do just that, but not yet.

It was several days later that Niles found Victoria in the little room.

"Well, well, well! What's all this?"

"Aunt Lucie thought it would be appropriate if I adopted this room."

"Tradition of the house, and all that?"

"Yes."

Niles frowned.

"Don't you like the room, Niles?"

"Oh, yes. It's all right."

"You haven't noticed."

"What?"

"The portraits."

"Oh . . . oh, I see. Isabella and—and Hippolyte. They're strange company—strange for you, and strange for each other." He laughed quietly.

"Aunt Lucie has been telling me——"

"I'll bet she has."

"Grandfather Julien has been telling me things, too."

Niles moved uneasily in his chair. "Listen, Vicky, I've got some things to tell you, too, things Grandfather and Aunt Lucie won't tell you."

"About what?"

"Well, old Isabella up there."

"She was your grandmother, Niles."

"Good Lord, you sounded exactly like Aunt Lucie then."

"Go on."

"Well, I'll bet Aunt Lucie didn't tell you that Isabella was the complete hellcat, did she?"

Victoria smiled a little. "Well, hardly."

"Well, she was. She was a holy terror."

"How so?"

"She was narrow, self-righteous, bigoted to the last degree, self-willed, and strong—and cruel. Why, Victoria, do you realize that singlehanded she turned this family from Catholic to Protestant?" He snapped his fingers, "Just like that."

"Did that make any special difference, really?"

"Catholics are happier than Protestants. And Grandfather—she spoiled his life. He wanted to go on being some kind of scientist. That was the day, Victoria, of the gentleman scholar. Some of them did important work. But she wanted the glory of White Cloud restored. That effort took money. He tried to make it. She—well, sort of dammed him up, shut him off, closed him in, until he was stagnant. That's not good for a Grandolet."

Niles looked up at the portrait. "I don't like the sight of her. She made weaklings of her children, both Aunt Lucie and my father. Look at her! I think she's terrible."

"No, no, Niles! There's something more there, something close to majesty."

"She'd have loved you for that word." He twisted about in his chair. "Vicky, while she lived she was more Grandolet than anybody—in the worst sense of the family tradition—she was White Cloud, she and no one else. No one else had a show."

"But Grandfather Julien——"

"Oh, I know how he talks, and how he won't talk. Sense of *noblesse oblige* and all that. I bet he hated her. He had to. Listen, Victoria, there is one thing about White Cloud you don't understand at all."

"What is it, Niles? I want to understand it completely."

"Do you?" He looked at her curiously. "You and I came too late, Victoria. The show is over."

"I don't understand."

"Don't you? Remember the first night you were here? We sat outside in the moonlight. Remember how White Cloud looked? The big house with all of its windows dark?"

"I don't remember it that way."

"But that's the way it was. That's what I was thinking of. In its own day the house would have been blazing from top to bottom. There would have been a house party, lots of people, music, maybe. But there it was—like a tomb. Not a sound, and one lonely light burning in Aunt Lucie's room."

"But I also remember that you said you couldn't live anywhere else."

"I couldn't. But I'm not mistaken about what is here and what isn't."

"Oh, Niles——"

"No, I have to talk. White Cloud, as Grandfather and Aunt Lucie imagine it, doesn't exist. There is no such place."

"Niles—what are you so excited about? I never heard you——"

"No one else did, either. It's this. All of the dead and gone family are hung about the neck of the present. There are a lot of families like us. They think the same way. They don't think of a future—God, they don't even think of the present. They think of the past, and so they *are* the past. We *are* the Grandolets because we don't think of anything else. And the old Grandolets and all our tributaries add up to something pretty dark."

"Your grandfather said almost the same thing."

"There are moments when he knows it well enough. The

[79]

old life, the old times—yes, there was grace and beauty and charm and all of that, but these rested on a dreadful foundation. Now, listen, I'm not talking like a Northerner, mind you. I'm talking about something that's deeper than the old questions which brought on a war—a war that was a second big wrong on top of the first one. I'm talking about what happened to us, the Grandolets, when we had too much money, when our fortunes and our gaiety rested on slavery, and the inevitable inhumanity that follows."

Victoria tried to interrupt, but Niles was having a say.

"I'd have been just like them if I'd lived then. And I'm a Southerner, don't forget, through and through, but I am also a realist. This is 1900, Victoria. A new century is coming up over the horizon. White Cloud is an anachronism, but in one sense only. We lost something too great to be estimated. There was courage, and there was dreaming, and integrity, too."

"You aren't being very consistent, Niles."

"We were not consistent, and we aren't now. But always there has been the strange flower of beauty on the dark tree of human life. I don't understand it, either. But it was here. White Cloud is here to prove it. But it is honestly true, Vicky, what I said—the show is over. We're too late."

Victoria shivered at his tone of voice. This was a Niles she did not know. She drew back a little from what she heard.

He went on, speaking gently. "Isabella Niles didn't understand that—when the curtain came down. Aunt Lucie doesn't even know it. She is still waiting for another act."

He glanced at the other portrait. "Hippolyte! He would have understood, that is if I understand him—and I think I do."

Victoria listened. She was stiffening her mind against everything Niles had said. *No, no, she was saying to herself, I will not be too late. I will be like Isabella. I will be White Cloud myself.*

Victoria sat very still for a long time after Niles had gone. She was remembering all he had said, but she was making her own kind of application of it.

She knew, as she sat there, that she was far from the girl Niles had married out of school just a few months ago. But she did not know clearly what she had become. What that was she must know, and quickly.

Slowly, almost imperceptibly, Victoria saw and felt herself change. Magically, she was becoming something. She did not know from what strange sources these changes were stemming. But even as she watched she saw the outlines take shape, take clearer form, still half defined, still half guessed, curiously portentous.

White Cloud! A place whose beauty she could not quite interpret herself! A being she could not in any way foretell. She felt the impulse of her own change, her own potentialities, but no profile of herself emerged.

If she could only know what she brought to this secret metamorphosis, she might direct, she might be the mistress of her own destiny, but there—there was the hidden place in her own personality that she could not know. She could not guess, even, nor could anyone else.

Her secret, she had thought once, might set her free—free of everything that bound people to a self-imposed pattern of a past. As Niles had said, the Grandolets were bound. But she was free to be, to become, anything she wished.

And now, even as she sat there in the fading afternoon, the first faint lines of profile did indeed begin to define themselves.

The clouds of her undetermined self began to draw together, to take shape. Here—here at White Cloud were the forces she might choose for her own determination. There on the wall, Isabella Niles and Hippolyte d'Aupais, contradictory, but both of them strong. Arrogant, determined, above the law.

She closed her hand, tight, until the knuckles whitened, and beat softly on the arm of the chair.

She had not told Niles, but she knew she was going to have a child. And now she was a Grandolet—a Grandolet in a stronger sense than Niles, or Aunt Lucie, or old Julien, even, could know. This afternoon she had seen the incredible composite of the family personality, she had seen it clear, and she was not afraid to look at it.

The beauty of White Cloud, yes, its aristocratic grace and distinction, its clear command to pride. The old dark order— what of it? Was it not drawn from intelligence and strength? Did it not proffer, openly, the right to dominion?

Isabella Niles. She had appeared and the destiny of the Grandolets had changed. She had passed, and they were only what she had made them.

She, Victoria Dunstan, was a Grandolet, too, deeply in the currents of her blood a Grandolet.

So much that she had partially resented at first turned suddenly into assets of power. She had hated that sentence of Aunt Lucie's about the bed—*Niles was born there, and his father and his grandfather.*

Very well, her own son would be born there. Julien Quintin Grandolet, she decided. She glanced at the portrait of Isabella. Yes, she whispered, even you, Isabella Niles, even you and your name are going out of the Grandolet family.

Victoria pressed her fingers hard against her temples. A dull, pulsing pain was making her miserable. She brought her shoulders up in her characteristic quick shrug. She was being feverish and excited. She was overwrought and giving herself over to melodrama. Her face set stubbornly, and she thrust the mood and the half-spoken soliloquies away from her.

It is only a house, she said to herself. It is a house and nothing more. The people who lived here long ago are dead. Nothing remains of them. They are unable to hinder—or to help. This time belongs to—to whoever wishes to use it.

She straightened in her chair, blinked and looked about, half smiling as if she had had to present an argument—a self-evident argument—to someone.

She arose, swaying a little with dizziness. She felt herself turn cold and sick, and wondered if she was going to faint. She reached out instinctively for something to hold to. Her hand fell on Orlou's outstretched arm.

"Yes, ma'am. You'll be all right in a minute. Just rest against me a little."

"Where—I didn't hear you come in, Orlou."

"No, ma'am. I'm always close by. Can you walk all right now?"

"Yes, I think so. I just felt a little——"

"Yes, ma'am."

Orlou helped her up the stairs and to bed. Victoria watched her. She wondered if Orlou knew she was a little frightened. The inscrutable face looked more like the sibyl than ever.

"You told Mr. Niles yet, Miss Victoria?"

"No. I guess I wasn't sure——"

"I'd tell him. It's a fine thing for White Cloud."

Victoria tried to smile.

"You're scared a little, Miss Victoria. Everybody is the first time. No need. It's right. White Cloud—*c'est un endroit de la fécondité*. Things that don't bear on this place die."

Orlou stroked her arm, and in a few minutes Victoria's disquiet subsided. Reassurance moved softly along her nerves. The words re-echoed in her fading consciousness: *"C'est un endroit de la fécondité.* Things that don't bear on this place die."

Presently she was asleep.

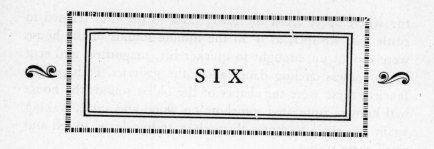

SIX

OFTEN, AS VICTORIA PASSED to and from her rooms, she paused on the gallery with her hand on the balustrade. Here, in some way she could not clearly define to herself, she felt that she was closer to the still enigmatic personality of the house. She wondered sometimes if she could ever think of White Cloud as simply a house. Perhaps not. Aunt Lucie did not think of it in such terms, nor did Orlou. Grandfather Julien did not, but Grandfather Julien was something of a poet. She liked to stand here and let her imagination run free; but, with a caution that hid deep within her, she liked to know when she was imagining, and when she was the sentient recipient of special communications. There were times when she knew well that she was playing a game, giving herself over to a luxury of make-believe, but there were other times when she felt certainly that the beautiful old house was vibrant with a life of its own. Perhaps it was only echoing, in some still unknown, unidentifiable way, the overtones of hates and passions greater and more enduring than the living bodies which had bred them.

She stood quite still, tilting her head a little to one side, in a pose that was becoming characteristic.

From this point, near the stairway, she had discovered that

the whole space from the lower floor to the roof seemed to rustle and whisper, as if all the minute sounds of the house were caught up, brought to quicker life, magnified, and sent in an endless circling dance about the galleries. Perhaps, she fancied, these were the shapes of the oldest sounds the house had known, impressed somehow on wood and stone, waking again and again to renew themselves, to live again, to tell and retell their stories.

At first, Victoria remembered, the unbroken silence of White Cloud had oppressed her a little; but it had not been long before she realized that the place was never silent. There were nearly always sounds from the garden, smothered half sounds from the quarters, or from the river, but even when these died down or were not separately discernible, White Cloud whispered—day and night the whole house whispered.

She wondered if it dreamed. Was it reciting to itself its long story of love and grief, of pain and desolate waiting, when, as Aunt Lucie had said, no one came to White Cloud at all, when there was only the river and the white house watching?

Or—Victoria shook her head impatiently, trying to dispel the mood of half-superstitious reverie. Lately she had found it easier and easier to fall into the way of Orlou's natural belief and acceptance of things just beyond the periphery of daylight reason. Just now—this moment—listening to the muted flutter of maybe imaginary sounds that seemed to come from everywhere, she began to wonder if they were an expression of acceptance or of warning.

She smiled. This was morbid and—symptomatic: she was going to have a child, and everything about her own self, mind and body, seemed already strange. But she tilted her head again and listened, and as she listened, her smile faded.

She was watching the chandelier. It was alive with points of colored fire. It swayed very slowly as if it were a giant pendulum linked to time, and very slowly it turned.

Victoria moved a little and leaned her head against one of the delicate columns supporting the upper gallery. She had tried so often to trace the intricate design of the crossing and interlacing crystals, but her vision was never quite equal to it. She found her attention held to a single pendant deep in the bewildering intricacy—a lone crystal that blazed for a moment with an intolerable ruby light, and then, as the chandelier moved, she saw it change to emerald, purple, gold, and go out as if a hand had quenched it.

Aunt Lucie had said that first day, "It is never still—never." But then it had seemed merely a huge, festive glitter. Now she had learned more of its changing moods. It was never still, that was true, and it was never twice the same.

The single pendant flared again, and Victoria saw a wall luster catch the reflection, burn for an instant in the half-dark, and wink, like an answering signal.

Occasionally Aunt Lucie saw her, noted her expression, and spoke of it afterward. "I declare, I do think Victoria is wonderfully beautiful. There is such a shining something about her. She's so white and—and transparent-looking. It's pleasant to know there's a beautiful mistress of White Cloud."

Victoria read Buffon to Julien. They were together more and more. Once or twice he was plaintive when the walks about the garden were too long for her. Aunt Lucie was solicitous. Niles was pleased about the baby, but now and then he asked meaningless questions, absent-mindedly, and studied her face with a puzzled look in his eyes. Then he would laugh and hurry away to the endless plantation duties that kept him from early morning until late afternoon.

The long, slow fall of Louisiana began. Victoria had looked forward to the season, remembering the exhilaration and tang of New England. But reviving weather never came. The fall was merely a lengthening of summer, drier, less hot, but of identical temper. The green faded, the woods across the river became rusty and dull, but the late-summer feeling persisted. In November points of red showed in the swamps, and a few vines streaked like a running fire through the trees. Muted tints of sienna and umber lay somber underfoot.

Victoria renewed her walks on the levee. Several times she had gone well out of sight of White Cloud. The dark woods deepened into swampy stretches. Somewhere, farther on, lay Far Félice. Niles had not yet taken her to see the place. It was some time before she discovered that she was never alone on these walks. Turning, she would see, far behind her, the stiff white figure of Orlou. Sometimes feeling herself too far from the house, she would hurry her step a little, only to see Orlou come out of hidden pathways and fall in behind her.

"Flora is coming!" Aunt Lucie rattled the large sheets of a voluminous letter. "She's in New Orleans and is coming up to White Cloud next week."

Victoria nodded slowly. "I had a letter, too, today."

"Oh, did you? Well, of course you would."

"It's the first letter I've had from her this summer."

Aunt Lucie looked ever so slightly embarrassed. "Oh, I have scarcely heard, either," she said airily. "She's been so excited being in Europe for the first time, flying around from place to place. My, my, it will be nice to see little Flora. You know her mother, Victoria?"

"I saw her twice at Fairfield——"

"Oh, yes, of course. I forgot. Marie—well, now, I think just between us, dear, I think Marie is a little difficult."

"She seemed very charming—and gracious."

"Certainly. She has good enough manners. But—a little"— Aunt Lucie laughed—"a little on the bossy side."

"Flora seemed pretty free, I should say."

"Winds her mother about her pinkie, just like that. The rest of us, too, for that matter. Everyone loves Flora. And now that people are getting back from Ponchartrain and the coast, we'll have some parties. It's time you met somebody. You must have the idea we live entirely alone in a wilderness."

"Niles, I do want to go up to Far Félice."

"All right, Vicky, first time I'm going that way. Any special reason?"

"Just curious."

"It's almost a ruin."

"So you said."

"You haven't seen Wyandotte, either."

"I'm more interested in Far Félice."

"As a matter of fact, I could go this afternoon. I need to see Greenwood."

"What's that?"

"Negro in charge up there."

"Oh, a person, not a place."

"Greenwood's a character. One of the best Negroes I ever knew. We hunted and fished together—rather, he took me when I was a kid. Greenwood is black as a bayou, wears earrings, but"—Niles shook his head thoughtfully—"but for an accident of color I'd say Greenwood is as good a man as anybody I know."

"What time can we go?"

"After dinner. You'll have to wear something a—a little less fancy, Vicky, if you want to walk around up there. Vines and weeds and so forth."

Niles helped Victoria to her seat in the light buckboard. "Now, let me see, Vicky. We can go the road just inside the levee. It takes us right up to the house, but I expect that's pretty rough through the swamp. I haven't been up that way in a couple of months. I guess we'd better take the back road." He clucked to the horses and they spun down the sandy side drive to the main road.

"You know, Niles, I've hardly been away from the house since I first came."

"Yes, I know, honey. It's been a tough summer for you."

"Oh, I didn't mean that. It hasn't been. White Cloud itself is inexhaustible—for me."

"Yes. Grandfather Julien has been telling you a lot, I hear."

"I'm fascinated by the history of the place, and the family, too."

"We're a queer lot. You must have found that out."

The road ran through cane fields for a long distance, then turned abruptly right into wild-looking woods.

"This is Far Félice." Niles glanced rather distastefully about him. "Damn wilderness."

"What really happened to Far Félice, Niles? Everyone is so reticent about it."

"Nothing so secret. I told you about the death of Quintin and his brother. White Cloud was built, about ready for occupancy, when that happened. Quintin's uncle Etienne moved into White Cloud and raised Grandfather Julien, who was just two years old at the time. Another brother, Octave, lived on at

Far Félice until the war. He was along in years, of course, but he went on with a local company and was killed at Vicksburg. Far Félice was closed then."

"No one has lived there since?"

"No. Everything was taken out and it's boarded up."

"Orlou is always so peculiar about the place."

"Orlou? Yes, of course. The Negroes are superstitious about the house. The stories have grown. Nothing to them. The place has suffered from floods. We have no way to drain and reclaim a lot of valuable land—I mean we haven't got enough money to do it. I'm getting timber out of the swamps now."

The road was almost lost from time to time in its winding way through woods and swamps. Low-hanging vines whipped at them, and once they had difficulty pulling through a soft, muddy stretch.

"We're coming to the cemetery, Vicky."

"Where? I don't see——"

"Just around the bend of the road."

They drove on for a few minutes. Victoria saw the gleam of white through the trees.

"There they are—all of the Grandolets, honey."

"Heavens, Niles! Such a lot of them!"

"Yes. They bring them back from all over. Want to get out and look?"

"Yes."

The cemetery seemed as large as many Victoria had seen placed close to country churches in New England. There was a low brick wall and inside, arranged in neat little streets, the close rows of vaults. Some of them were quite large. The cemented doors had crosses on them—all except a few. She looked inquiringly at Niles.

"The crosses?"

"Yes."

"After Isabella, my dear. No more popery or holy symbols."

"Oh, yes. I forgot."

The great oaks towered overhead, and the long streamers of moss added to the somber atmosphere of the place.

"It's so peaceful."

"Yes, Vicky, I guess that's one reason why I never have dreaded death. I think I don't, really. It's all so sort of friendly and cozy. We know all of these people. They're just there, inside of those doors. All of their worries over and done with. You see, we even remember what those worries were, and we can stop and congratulate the old boys they don't have to think about 'em any more."

They walked back and forth among the tombs, stopping to read names—so many of the same names Victoria had read on the portraits at White Cloud.

Niles sighed. "I like it here. Only the seasons pass by, one after the other, and the new Grandolets come along to pay visits as we are doing now. No one remembers their sins. Sometimes I find myself hoping they enjoyed their sins while they were alive."

Victoria stopped at a large vault with marble obelisks at the four corners. "Look, Niles! Hippolyte!"

"Yep. There he is. And look, right back of him is Isabella. Funny, when you think of them lying quietly so close together. The world wouldn't have held the two of them in life. But we'd better hurry, Vicky. Come on."

Niles pointed to an opening in the trees. "Those are the Far Félice quarters." A double row of brick cabins huddled under an irregular canopy of giant live oaks.

"Look, Niles. Does anyone live there? I see——"

"Oh, yes. There are a lot of Far Félice Negroes yet. But they stay away from the big house. Hard to get one in there for anything."

They drove the length of the "street," as Niles called it. "Now, there's the house."

Victoria could see little of it. Tall pink chimneys were half hidden by vines, and the house itself was completely screened by magnificent oaks.

"Whoa! We'll have to get out here."

An enormous Negro came out from a tumbled-down outbuilding of some sort.

"Greenwood!"

"Yes, Mistuh Niles."

"I'm going in to look at the house. Greenwood, you haven't seen Miss Victoria?"

"No, suh. I'm mighty proud to see you, ma'am. I heerd about you. They say Mistuh Niles plum outmarry heself."

Greenwood chuckled and led the horses away. Victoria thought she had never heard a kinder, gentler voice.

"Niles, isn't he nice?"

"Who? Oh, Greenwood. He's pure gold. Now, let's see. We'd better go in the side—this way."

Niles looked back. "Greenwood!"

"Yes, Mistuh Niles."

"Come along. I might want you to kill a few snakes."

"Oh, Niles!"

"It's all right, Vicky. Keep your eye out. That's all."

The garden was completely overgrown. An indescribable tangle of vines draped the trees and bound them together. A semicircle of crape myrtles still stood in an unbroken rank at one side. The brilliant colors burned like torches under the gray-green shadows of the oaks and magnolias.

"What is that, Niles?"

"What? The building? That's a *pigeonnier*. There's another on the other side of the house. Feature of these houses."

The beautiful, octagonal, towerlike structure seemed to stagger under a weight of wistaria that had already destroyed the pointed roof and torn away the ornamental brick coping.

They walked on cautiously, stepping high through the tall grass which was turning a soft rusty pink.

"Here we are!"

Victoria looked up. She had seen only the deep wooden wings in the rear of the house. Now, the long-columned façade stood suddenly above her. Even with its boarded windows and its sagging ruin, Far Félice kept its look of grandeur. There were a central stair and two curving end ones leading to the marble-flagged gallery. As they mounted the stairs, their steps echoed from the heavily paneled ceiling two and a half stories above them. Rusted wrought-iron balconies were set at the long row of second-story windows.

"Operatic, isn't it?" Niles smiled a bit ruefully at the spectacle. "Think you can open that door, Greenwood?"

"I 'spec' so, suh." The heavy double doors scraped open. "Dey wasn't even fasten up."

"Come on, Vicky, let's look. I haven't been in here since I was a kid."

Victoria went ahead with a queer feeling stirring inside of her.

The floor was covered with debris, and most of the ceiling had fallen, but there were some areas of a landscape wallpaper still clinging to the cracking plaster. It portrayed over and over in diagonal rows a sad-faced damsel looking out from a floral casement.

"Marianna of the Moated Grange, I'd say." Niles poked at the loose paper.

"Niles, it's priceless. I want to rescue some of it, if it will hold together."

"All right, all right. Another day. There are the doorknobs, too. Silver."

"Really?"

"Yep. Grandfather Julien says leave 'em alone. Guess we could use them, though. I think Yankees buy such things. Oh, sorry, Victoria."

"I'm not a Yankee."

"Not any more, anyway."

Beyond, in the long dining room, a chandelier half denuded of its crystals strove to answer the glimmer of light.

"This house could be restored." Victoria spoke dreamily.

"At a cost, my darling."

"But gradually. Could we look upstairs?"

"I guess the stairway is sound." He tried it, bouncing on the steps. "Like a rock. Come on."

Upstairs there was the same wreckage. But there was visible the indestructible outline of elegant and gracious proportions.

"First they would have to fix the roof to prevent further deterioration. Would that be too much to begin with?"

"Are you serious, Vicky? What for, for goodness' sake? We've already got ten times more house than we need at White Cloud."

"I don't know, Niles. I feel something about this place—an affinity."

"Stuff. I think it's spooky——"

"*Yes, suh.*" Greenwood spoke suddenly.

"Hants." Niles spoke solemnly.

"*Yes, suh.*"

"Ah——" Victoria was about to jeer when she caught Greenwood's expression.

"Mistuh Niles, *you* know 'bout 'at 'ere *garçonnière,* de one in de nawth side uh de house."

"I don't recollect."

"Well, suh, dey's a big roun' room down under hit, an' all de winduhs got big, thick iron bars at 'em."

"Oh, yes. I know."

"Well, suh, I ain' know *whut* it wuz use foh back in slavery times, but all de same won' none of de doahs stay shut. No, suh, you can shut 'em up tight, an' nex' mawnin' dah dey is, spang wide open."

"What do you suppose——" Victoria spoke timidly.

"Well, ma'am, I done hear dat back in slavery times de over-seeah used to lock up de slaves in dere an' whup 'em. Now you cain't *keep* a doah shut. De sperrits come back an' open 'em up. Yes, ma'am."

"That's a whopper of a story, Greenwood. I know what that room was used for."

"Yes, suh?"

"It was a storeroom. Plantations used to have to keep lots of supplies. That's why it was barred. Anyhow, slaves weren't whipped at the house—but off somewhere—when it had to be done."

"Yes, suh. But you cain't shut de doahs no moah. Dey's jes' spang wide open nex' mawnin'."

"Well, well. Now let's go down and around to the north side. That's where a wing of the house was burned."

"Mistuh Niles, kin I go back to de horses now?"

"Yes, go ahead. We'll be there in a minute."

Greenwood hurried away.

"Even Greenwood won't stay about here more than he can help."

Victoria stood in the door for a moment, looking up at the

mammoth columns and then out across the overgrown gardens toward the levee which lay like a sleeping monster not a hundred yards from the house.

"If they ever have to move the levee again this house will go into the river."

"How terrible! How simply terrible!"

"If we could just get the Federal government to do something about flood control, straighten the channel, build spillways—but you can't get anything for Louisiana."

"Why?"

"We're still a conquered people. Now, don't get a mistaken idea about what I think. I'm not asking help from anyone. We'll get along somehow. We made it in the first place, and, by God, we'll make it over again."

Victoria had never seen Niles look as he did at this moment. His face was dark, brooding, angry, and defiant.

"Listen, honey. Greenwood is half right. There's something about Far Félice. It's like a shadow—I don't know how to say what I mean—like a shadow that reaches out and out and on and on through the generations. It touches White Cloud."

Victoria was only half listening. She seemed to be absorbed in a rush of her own thinking.

"What's the matter, Vicky?"

"I love it, Niles."

"Love Far Félice?"

"Yes. Listen, Niles, does Far Félice belong to you, just to you?"

"Yes, of course."

"What are you going to do with it?"

"Nothing."

"Niles!"

"Yes, Vicky."

"Give it to me."

He gasped and looked hard at her. "Why—my darling child, it is already yours."

"I know, but I mean just the house—I feel *kin* to it."

"All right. Far Félice belongs to you. It's yours for keeps. Gosh, I'll take it out of the estate if you want it that way."

"No. Just *say* it's mine."

"Far Félice is yours. Now let's go see the real ruin."

The north wing of the house was a shell, completely burned out, and now covered with a thick blanket of green.

"That's where Quintin Grandolet and his brother Paul died in the library—there where the end room was. Grandfather Julien says there is a curse on every brick of it. You see the swamps are coming in after it. The river is waiting just on the other side of the levee. It's doomed—like everything of its kind. Better stay clear of it, honey. I don't think I'm superstitious, but I don't know about Far Félice."

"I love it."

"Still?"

"Yes."

"Still want it?"

"Yes."

"What'll you do with it?"

"I'll—next year, after the baby comes, I'll begin restoring it— just what I can. The place will furnish some help, won't it?"

"All you want."

"Then——"

"It's yours, Victoria."

They stood quite still for a few moments. One would have said that here was the perfect illustration of the triumph of the earth over the little work of man's pride.

"Listen, Niles, what is that?"

"Negro singing somewhere, I guess."

A voice, high and thin, was singing a wild cadenza of eerie figures. The primitive coloratura gradually subsided into words.

Victoria listened, only half understanding the odd patois.

> *Ou, Toucoutou, mo connin vous,*
> *Ou, Toucoutou, mo connin vous,*
> *Vou cet in morico—*

There was more that she could not understand. Then, in contrast, the voice dropped into English.

> *If I had my way, oh Lawdy, Lawdy,*
> *If I had my way, oh Lawdy, Lawdy,*
> *If I had my way, oh Lawdy, Lawdy,*
> *I'd tear the building down.*

Niles laughed aloud, and the spell of the afternoon was broken. "Appropriate enough, I'd say. Come on, let's go."

Victoria went reluctantly, stopping again and again to look back at the towering mass of Far Félice, its blind windows and its silent galleries.

All the way home she continued to ask herself bewildered questions. She was trying to understand what was really her puzzling state of mind, for she knew with unescapable clarity that she felt herself arrayed against something, or somebody, but what or who or why, she did not know.

She thought of White Cloud—the Grandolets. She had come to the place with a deep misgiving. Indeed, it was a basic misgiving that included doubts of her own self. Several times in her life she had had to stare down the blasting fact of her unknown origin, and corollary to it, her unknown self. For a long time she had been profoundly shaken by it. Then she had made over out of the lack of concrete information a source of strength and self-reassurance.

White Cloud itself, the house with its half-mystical existence in the minds of the Grandolets, and its half-mystical impact upon her own consciousness, had been a factor wholly unexpected in character and in effect. It had been an unpredictable factor: it was still an unpredictable factor. White Cloud: could she feel that it had taken her to itself, as the Grandolets had graciously and with simpleheartedness accepted her? She stopped to correct herself. The Grandolets, Grandfather Julien and Aunt Lucie, had been gracious, but maybe not so simplehearted. She found herself counting Orlou in.

Southerners, she had decided long ago at Fairfield, seem simpler than they are.

Orlou, now. There was no fault discernible in Orlou's seeming devotion. But was it a devotion of the personal kind that her hungry ego demanded, or was it too much indeed like Grandfather Julien's own habit of *noblesse oblige?* Orlou's care might well be for the Grandolets, for the house, the tradition, the family, of which, in Orlou's eyes, she might appear no more than an incident.

It had been in this way, she thought, that in spite of herself there had grown up this—this exciting sense of contest. She paused as that word crossed her musing. *Exciting.* Yes, it was exciting. She felt now as if she had been waiting all of her young and unformed life for this major contest to appear.

Victoria shook herself impatiently. Niles did not notice. He had fallen into a reverie of his own—business affairs, no doubt. He was driving home through the rapidly thickening dusk with his eyes half closed, his attention wholly withdrawn.

Again she tried to reassert a common-sense dominion over her stubborn intuitions. Contest? she asked herself. Contest, for heaven's sake, with what? Nothing appeared against her. She was the wife of Niles Grandolet, and that, she now knew, was far better than anything she could have hoped for and something, in this countryside, of real importance. She had every assurance of family friendship and support—except Flora, maybe. She came up short in her free reconnaissance: Flora!

The feeling that struck at her suddenly from ambush was not conscience or any faint relation to remorse. No. She had to remember that she had known she was taking Niles from Flora. True, Flora herself had said that Niles was not in love with her, that he had never spoken, and so on and on, in Flora's characteristic habit of diluting information and emotion alike with sheer quantity of talk. But she had seen that Flora did care and that Flora did hope.

But she had little enough concern for Flora or Flora's feelings. Flora had so much, and she had nothing. No: what she was feeling was—was—it was *fear!* Victoria was startled, but her heart and brain were both quick to recognize that chill visitor. Fear? What had she to fear? What *could* she fear from Flora—pretty little, fluffy Flora?

Victoria's cool, accurate brain answered, clearly and at once. Flora was one of the Grandolets. Even Grandfather Julien softened when he spoke of her. Aunt Lucie had revealed plainly enough that Flora was something more than a dear cousin. And Niles? Was it not a little strange how reticent Niles was on the subject of Flora? He was usually talkative enough about everything and everyone. Nor had Flora written to her all of this summer, until this one short note had come. It was not to be overlooked either that Flora had simply announced her visit, quite as if she were coming to her own home. But of course she *was* one of the family connections. Of course—and that was the crux of her own unease at the moment.

Flora's coming, the character of her relationship, actual and sentimental, to the Grandolets, all contributed at this moment to the feeling of forces and persons drawn up on opposing sides. Maybe, after all, this was no more than a symptom of her present condition. Women always had queer fancies, did they not? She had read something like that. And Orlou seemed to take it for granted that she was already a capricious and unaccountable person.

"Niles!"

"Yes, honey?"

"Are you glad?"

"Of what?"

"That we're going to have a baby?"

He laid his brown hand firmly over hers. "Do you have to ask? Didn't I tell you? Of course I am, of course."

"I just wanted you to say so."

"My dear child." His tone was gentle, his look kind. There was nothing of the familiar small fire of passion in his eyes. She was relieved that there would be no more of that for a while.

She settled comfortably in her seat. After a moment she turned and looked back along the darkening road they had traveled.

There was Far Félice. Again her reluctant fancy leaped to the notion that a secret ordering of obscure forces was in way. She dwelt upon the idea, darkly, intensely, with a morbid acuity.

Far Félice. A thin tocsin sounded in her brain, but it was

not a signal of alarm; it was again the familiar call of excitement that was part disquiet and part something else—triumph, maybe. Because, she felt with certainty, she had found something today. She had found an ally, and that ally was Far Félice. Ally against what she could not say, but she knew that she was no longer alone, no longer powerless against whatever might come.

The crunching of the wheels in the deeply rutted road made a sleepy sound. Her half-dreaming fancy was running back over the fragments of the Far Félice story. Suddenly, her attention snagged on a detail. Quintin and his brother Paul had quarreled and killed each other because of a woman—Quintin's wife.

"Niles!"

"Yes, honey?"

"Who was Quintin Grandolet's wife?"

"Which—oh, you mean Great-grandfather Quintin?" Niles did not look at her.

"Yes, of course. Who was she?"

"Her name was Jeannette Vélazy."

"Vélazy? Flora's family?"

"Yes."

Victoria felt as if she had suddenly stepped from solid ground into space. She could not explain to herself her deep sense of shock. She coaxed her faculties together. They had scattered like birds when the shadow of a hawk passes quickly over them. Vélazy! Again—a faint, faraway threat. She smiled fleetingly, a quick, disdainful smile. Flora!

She frowned and thought for a moment. "That's curious, isn't it?"

"What's curious?"

"Didn't I see Jeannette Vélazy's tomb back there?"

"Yes, of course."

"I noticed the date, Niles."

"Well?"

"She died first."

"Ye-es. I guess I did know that. I forgot."

"But you told me the brothers killed each other because of her."

"They did."

"*After* her death?"

Niles looked blank. "It seems so, doesn't it? Well, I'll be damned. Victoria, I never paid much attention to those old tales. I may have something down wrong. That is curious, isn't it?"

"Very curious, Niles."

As they turned into the White Cloud drive Niles remarked: "We have visitors."

"How do you know?"

"Those bay horses up there by the barn. They look like— yes, they belong to Bart Molloy at Oquipah. Bart's got kind of a transfer business. Must have brought somebody over."

No one was in sight as they entered the house except Emsy, who was fluttering about the dining-room door.

"Somebody come, Emsy?"

"Yes, suh, Mr. Niles. Miss Flora done come."

"Miss Flora! Why, I thought she was coming Tuesday."

"Yes, suh. She had a chance to come up to Oquipah with Miss Neilly, so she jes' come on ahead of time."

"Well, well. That's fine. Where is she?"

"She's up in Miss Lucie's room, takin' off her things. She jes' got heah a few minutes ago."

"Come on, Vicky, let's see."

Victoria followed Niles, but she did not hurry. Niles rapped on Aunt Lucie's door, and in an instant Flora flung herself at him with a burst of chatter and a shower of little-girl kisses.

"Niles, darling. I am so happy. You look grand. Where is Vicky?"

"Here, Flora."

"Oh, my, Vicky—isn't it wonderful? Here we are at White Cloud! Oh, I've missed everybody so, and I was so homesick! Vicky, you look wonderful. Just imagine—here you are at White Cloud! Think of it, Aunt Lucie, Vicky's at White Cloud! Oh, come in, come in—Aunt Lucie and I have been talking so fast!"

Everyone laughed, and the room was filled with the staccato of lightning-speed French. Father Julien sat by the window. He nodded to Victoria. "Sit here, Victoria. Isn't it wonderful to see Flora again?"

Aunt Lucie fluttered about picking up things and putting them down again.

"Now let me see, Flora, I guess you'll stay back here in the corner rooms next to me."

"Anywhere, darling, just——"

Victoria's voice broke in evenly. "I asked Pinky to have the rose room ready for Flora, Aunt Lucie."

There was an instant of silence. Aunt Lucie looked at the floor for a moment.

"Why, of course. I didn't think. You'll want Flora where the two of you can talk before you go to bed. You'll have so much to say, won't you?"

Flora laughed, a shade too gaily. "Anywhere at all. I'm at home any place in White Cloud. Oh, I'm so happy to be back! I'm going to stay a long, long time."

"You must," Victoria answered in the same level tone. She arose. "I'll send Laurine up to help you, Flora."

"Oh—oh, thank you. Any one of the girls. They all know me."

"Laurine will be up in a minute. I'll run along and dress. Niles and I have just been up to Far Félice."

Supper that night was somehow not quite an easy affair. Flora broke into gales of talk, and then as quickly subsided. Victoria made herself consciously remote, as if her mind were more than half occupied with other and far more important concerns.

After dessert Flora leaned back in her chair with an expression rather like childish guilt.

"I have something to tell you!"

Aunt Lucie looked startled. "What now, child?"

"I guess you'll have to stop calling me child from now on."

Victoria caught her breath. She knew what was coming.

"Flora!" Niles' expression was curious.

"Yes, Niles. Maybe you can guess."

"No."

"I—I'm going to be married."

Aunt Lucie clapped her hands. Suddenly she arose, went around the table, and kissed Flora on both cheeks. "My little Flora. What a happiness!"

"But"—Flora's big brown eyes looked almost hurt—"you do not ask who!"

"Well—who?" Niles' words crackled a little.

"You do not know him."

Everyone laughed.

"He is—he is beautiful. You will like him. I met him on the steamer, imagine that, and all the time he is of Louisiana."

"Flora—who?"

"His name is, I think maybe Niles you know the name of his family—it is not a wonderful name, but he is so nice—even Mama likes him."

Niles threw up his hands. "Take your time, honey, of course we would like to know——"

"Oh, yes—his name is John Connor."

"Connor?" Aunt Lucie frowned. "I don't believe I ever knew a Connor family in Louisiana, except, yes, there were some Connors who bought the Rennover place——"

"It is the same, the same. He lives at Rennover."

"Who were his people? Do you know anything about them, Flora?"

"Mama knows everything. She asked John all the questions. John's mother was Barbara Cheer."

"Oh, my dear, of course. She's a distant cousin of our own Dr. Cheer. I remember. Why, that's very nice, indeed."

"It is the same. He says he knows Dr. Cheer a little."

Niles spoke gravely. "Every happiness in the world, Flora. It's actually hard to realize you're old enough to be married."

"I'm as old as Victoria, exactly."

The talk arose, subsided, and arose again.

"But there is another piece of news, and this is one of the best."

Aunt Lucie leaned forward. "You are going to live in Louisiana—so we can see you often—that's it, is it not?"

"Better. We have decided to live at Wyandotte."

"Wyandotte!"

Victoria saw Aunt Lucie and Niles exchange a swift glance.

"But, my darling Flora, how wonderful! No one has lived at Wyandotte for ever and ever so long. At Wyandotte! We will see you all the time."

"Yes. John thought it would be better to lease Rennover since Wyandotte is much the better place, and I like to be here near White Cloud, and all of you—and Vicky."

That night Victoria seemed unable to break Niles' heavy mood.

"Niles!"

"Yes, Vicky."

"I thought Aunt Lucie was rather startled when Flora said she was coming to Wyandotte. Why?"

"Well," Niles rubbed the back of his head, "I guess—oh, I don't know."

"Yes, you do. What is it?"

"Well, Vicky, I've been running Wyandotte—or rather *we* have—for a long time."

"Yes?"

"The truth is, Victoria, that nearly half of our income is straight from Wyandotte."

"Will that make a lot of difference to—you?"

"Yes, I guess it will. We simply leased it, and hardly paid more than the general upkeep of the place. There wasn't anybody among the Vélazys to take care of it. During the last five years I have worked it up into a fine place."

"I'm sorry, Niles."

"Oh, that's all right. Heavens, the place belongs to Flora. They've been generous with us about it."

"But you'll have less work and responsibility, too."

"And a whole lot less money."

"You don't need a lot, do you?"

Niles looked at her quickly. "Doesn't money mean anything to you, Victoria?"

Victoria laughed. "Niles, I never had any. It doesn't mean anything to me. I love White Cloud—that's all."

"Gee, you make me feel a lot better. You know, a man likes——"

"I know all you want to say. But—this is the same White Cloud, and we are the Grandolets, and soon there'll be another one. It *has* to be a son, Niles."

"Gee, Vicky——"

"But, I do feel a little—not resentful exactly, but wondering——"

"What?"

"That you who work all the time should lose something, and that Flora should——"

"Wyandotte belongs to her. It's all right, but I guess——"

"What are you thinking about?"

"I'm just thinking about Far Félice. Maybe I'll have to get busy and see what I can do about it."

"Maybe it will live up to its name."

"It'll be the first time, if it does."

"Niles, you must talk more to me. Maybe sometimes I can be a help, too."

He nodded absently. "We can go after some of that timber in earnest, and maybe I could get to work on drainage and get some land back."

"I remember you said there were thousands of acres in White Cloud——"

"So much of it is useless. These places have heavy responsibilities, too. You have to take care of the Negroes through bad years."

"I see."

"I heard about an improved cane species they're experimenting with down around St. Vincent's. I'm going to look into it. Funny," he added after a moment's silence, "funny the way Far Félice seems to be coming back into our affairs. Far Félice —jinxes, hants, and all!"

SEVEN

FLORA'S MOTHER WAS, as Aunt Lucie had tactfully understated, rather difficult. She was a fragile, dry little person who looked older than she was. Presumably she had once been plump, but now she was thin with the deeply wrinkled look of recent deflation. She wore a great deal of jet, some fine jewelry, and was always enmeshed and entangled in a veritable puzzle of scarfs, veils, and the like.

"Oh," she said, as she was ushered into Victoria's "Isabella room," "do *you* use this now?"

"It seemed appropriate for the mistress of White Cloud to follow tradition." Aunt Lucie murmured the explanation with a warning firmness in her voice.

"Oh—well, yes, of course, but it is so hard to accustom oneself to new arrangements, isn't it?"

"It must be difficult as one grows old." Victoria smiled sweetly. "I am finding the many adjustments rather fun."

"Yes, I dare say. Oh, you've brought Isabella Niles down from the gallery."

"I fell in love with her."

"*You* did?"

"Oh, yes. I like to feel her spirit in this room."

"Hm. She was quite—quite a person."

"I can see that."

Mrs. Vélazy looked speculatively at Victoria. After a few moments, she said: "I meant to ask you, since you are in the family now, about your middle name. Lynn. Are you related to the Lynns of Savannah?"

"No. I have no Southern relatives."

"Oh, that's too bad."

"Why?"

"Well, it's always sort of homey to find relationships."

"It might be stuffy."

"Oh, my dear, my dear—not——"

"If they're nice people?"

"Why, yes—yes, exactly."

"You haven't any Northern relatives, have you?"

"Certainly not."

Victoria laughed. "Too bad."

Marie Vélazy looked angrily at Aunt Lucie.

Victoria leaned forward in her chair. "Listen, please. I was Flora's roommate for four years at school. I knew from the first day that she was everything well bred and charming. I didn't have to be told by way of her family connections. My father taught me quite early to recognize good breeding at sight."

"Of course, of course." Mrs. Vélazy was distinctly uneasy, and her glance traveled nervously from Victoria to Aunt Lucie and back again. "Your dear papa is an Episcopal clergyman, I recall. New Hampshire."

"Where we came from England."

"Oh, really——"

"He also taught me to reckon intelligence and the ordinary brand of politeness as somewhat more valuable than a tradition that had—er—been neglected."

Mrs. Vélazy looked as if she were about to cry.

"I'm sure I don't know what you mean."

Aunt Lucie spoke quickly, "Victoria means——"

"Let me explain, Aunt Lucie. I do wish—*Cousin* Marie to understand what I mean. I love Aunt Lucie and Grandfather Julien, and I love White Cloud. This turns out to be my home. I never heard of it, and knew nothing about it until I was married——"

"Well, well, my child——"

"And I never dreamed in my rather—shall I say ascetic?—bringing up that there could be any geographical boundaries for good manners, good family, or even good taste."

Marie Vélazy looked steadily at Victoria. Her fluttering quieted, and her hands lay perfectly still in her lap. She spoke gently, dropping into French as by instinct.

"I imagine I deserved a rebuke, but I do wish you to understand me, too. We are a garrulous and thoughtless people, my child, and we go on talking in the ways of our equally thoughtless ancestors. We actually do not think as well of ourselves as we seem to, nor of our families. God knows all of us have some terrible ones, haven't we, Lucie? You must overlook an old woman talking as we have all talked from the earliest times. You will discover that we insult each other with the greatest freedom. And now, Cousin Victoria, won't you give me some tea?"

She laughed easily, making a trilling sound so like Flora that it was amazing. All look of resentment faded from the little, tight-curled mouth. Marie Vélazy had been a beautiful girl, and for a fleeting moment a vanished charm rested like sunshine on her face. Victoria arose and pulled the bellcord. She felt suddenly helpless and entirely in the wrong.

"Pinky will bring tea. Maybe you'll excuse me. I know you two want to talk."

Marie laughed again, and laid her hand on Victoria's arm. "Nonsense. Sit down, Victoria Grandolet. I'm going over all the New Orleans scandal for Lucie. You might as well be initiate."

Tea was served presently, and the light running talk began. Now and then Marie Vélazy's eyes rested for the tiniest instant on Victoria's face.

Victoria did not recover from her discomfort. She had appeared uncertain, gauche, and stupidly defiant. She was sure that Flora's mother was making precisely that estimate of her, and at the same time condoning it, forgiving and accepting for the family's sake. Victoria would have given a great deal to know what Aunt Lucie thought.

The clear, tinkling French went on and on like an old-fashioned music box. Marie was witty, and Victoria recognized reluctantly that she had also a tried and well-seasoned wisdom that was precisely adjusted to the world in which she lived. Her descriptions and comments were delicately edged with a worldly malice.

" . . . And so I advise the children to be married at once. It's a worry to wait. I remember well." She giggled naughtily. "One should not place an undue tax on the impatience of children, though God knows I have come to believe that half of the proprieties of the world are all nonsense. Of course it would never do to say so. I don't know what would become of society—or the church."

"Are you fond of young Mr. Connor, Marie?"

"How should I know? He's personable. He looks strong and well. Maybe they'll have some good healthy children. But I don't think I ever really knew any Connors, did you, Lucie?"

"I've heard, it seems to me——"

"*Justement!* One hears of so many people. I am sure John Connor is a fine young man. He likes politics. He might be President—it seems anyone can be who tries hard enough—but, of course, we know perfectly well a Connor is not a Vélazy or a Grandolet."

She wagged her head sagely at Victoria. "Calling a spade a bad name—Victoria, I am sure you never had enough curiosity to ask or find out who I was?"

"No, I must say——"

"*Mais,* I will lay a wager, you've been wondering right now since I make so much talk."

Victoria blushed, and the little old lady gave a small triumphant shriek. "*Voilà!* Well," she looked impishly back over her shoulder at the painting on the wall, "my name was d'Aupais."

"Hippolyte——"

"Of the same breed, and bad enough, goodness knows. You know about him, I fancy."

"A little."

"A devil he was, like so many. His d'Aupais grandfather was an ancestor of mine."

"Is that still another connection between the Vélazys and the Grandolets?"

"Oh, my dear, the connections are numerous—one of them hardly orthodox——"

"Oh, Marie, Marie, that's only a tale——"

"It has persisted. It's been told all through the family for more than two hundred years."

"Well——"

"*Bien, bien!* We will forget—for now. Victoria, we are so

involved—some dozen families, or more—that many of our marriages smack of incest."

"Marie!" Aunt Lucie set her cup down with a bang.

"Tien! No harm. But that's one good reason for welcoming a Connor. There's no possible relationship *there.* Tell me, Victoria, why did you bring Hippolyte down to this room?"

"Just liked him."

"Hm. So many women did. Niles *does* look like him."

"But Niles is not like him in any other way." Aunt Lucie was ready for an argument.

Marie Vélazy was enjoying herself. She turned, disentangled the brilliant-studded chain of her lorgnettes from a snarl of lace and ribbons.

"Niles is different in every way." Aunt Lucie was plaintive, as if she did not expect to be heard.

"I wonder, I wonder. *Mon dieu,* he was handsome, wasn't he? No wonder the girls fairly leapt into bed with him."

"Marie! Remember—Victoria."

"Don't be silly, Lucie. There is no ice unbroken between Victoria and me. I fancy we understand each other perfectly."

She arose and began to collect her trappings. "Victoria, make a study of the family history. It's better than a storybook—there are no literary restrictions, you see! You'll come to New Orleans for the wedding, of course. After the honeymoon we'll have an old-fashioned house party at Wyandotte."

Aunt Lucie glanced quickly at Victoria. "I don't know, Marie, if Victoria should undertake the trip——"

"What? You don't mean? Why, that's perfect! My child, I do admire efficiency—and dispatch."

EIGHT

FLORA WAS MARRIED in New Orleans shortly before Christmas. The Christmas holidays saw a large house party at Wyandotte as Mrs. Vélazy had planned, but Victoria was unable to attend the wedding or to join the house party. Victoria was ill. Orlou and Aunt Lucie sat with her hour after hour trying to help ward off the paralyzing nausea that attacked her without cessation.

Dr. Cheer came almost daily through December. He recommended a specialist later on and Dr. Chaussegros of New Orleans was called.

"She's a healthy young woman, Mr. Grandolet," he said to Niles. "Not a thing in the world wrong with her. This isn't unnatural of course, except in its severity. And there's plenty of precedent for that, even. It may let up, it may not."

"Good heavens, Doctor, could she go on like this until May—until the baby is born?"

"She could, and she might."

"Could she stand it?"

"Oh, yes. It's very disagreeable, of course, and weakening, but she's a healthy girl."

"Lord!"

"Yes, I know it's distressing, but—do you mind if I ask you a few questions, Mr. Grandolet?"

"Certainly not. Go ahead."

"Is there any reason—do you know of any reason at all why Mrs. Grandolet might not want a child?"

"Why, no, none whatever."

"You're certain of that?"

"Yes, Dr. Chaussegros, I am—quite certain."

"Why?"

"Why am I certain? Well, for one thing, I know that Victoria wanted the child."

"Did she say so?"

"Yes, sir. We talked it over during the summer. In fact, it was her own wish that we should have a child right away."

"Curious."

"Why so? What's curious about it?"

"Well, nothing, really. Nothing I can put my finger on, exactly. But we're coming into a new kind of—of evaluation of old and familiar symptoms that have always been taken as a matter of course. An acute nausea, such as this, so steadily sustained is, as I said, certainly common enough. But we have found, in instances, that there are reasons in the mind."

"Oh, stuff!" Niles spoke almost hotly. "Victoria is as sound as——"

"Oh, you misunderstand me completely."

"But, I mean to say, she's so open and frank, and extremely matter-of-fact about the whole business."

Dr. Chaussegros pulled meditatively at his short pointed beard. He seemed not to be listening to Niles.

"Sometimes, for some obscure reason, a woman hates having a child, or hates something about it."

[117]

"Well, your theories don't apply. I can assure you of that."

"I think I'll stay on until tomorrow, Mr. Grandolet. Can you arrange for me to catch the noon train at Oquipah?"

"You'll have to make an early start from here."

"That's quite all right. I'd like to see Mrs. Grandolet again this afternoon and tonight."

Niles went out to the levee and stood looking at the river. The wind was chilly, but he thrust his hands in his pockets and set out walking briskly in the direction of Far Félice. He kept turning over and over in his mind those puzzling and disturbing questions of Dr. Chaussegros . . . Sometimes a woman hates having a child, *or hates something about it*. He stopped still for a moment, then he walked on slowly.

Niles was remembering. He had heretofore refused completely in his own mind to consider just how Victoria cared for him, how much, or how little. She had married him, hadn't she? Yes. And then, afterward? Again he tried to shy the question. It was darn curious, wasn't it, how little one knew about the ideas and the behavior of "nice" girls? Not so strange, maybe. Nobody talked about such things.

He walked on, rather blindly, stumbling now and then on the uneven pathway. Darn it! Why was he troubling? But all of the time a small icy question was pressing at the back of his attention. The insistent, relentless little question became almost like a physical pain.

He picked up a clod and threw it at the black mirror of a pool. Wasn't he being a fool? If he worried like this *now,* what would he do when the time came? But he knew that his worry was not entirely about Victoria's persistent illness. No! It had been awakened this afternoon by Dr. Chaussegros' indirection. These questions, he knew, veiled some other question that the doctor would not ask.

Dr. Chaussegros would not ask that question, he knew. No; and by God, *he* wouldn't ask it of himself, either.

But he was shaken and he knew it.

Niles went on until he came to Far Félice. He thought of the day he had brought Victoria here. Already that seemed a long time ago. Something was happening to him that he thought this way. As if something vital had changed. Nothing was changed. Everything was just as it was.

He smiled, remembering the song they had heard that day.

> *If I had my way, oh Lawdy, Lawdy,*
> *If I had my way, oh Lawdy, Lawdy,*
> *If I had my way, oh Lawdy, Lawdy,*
> *I'd tear the building down.*

Curious fool song, wasn't it? He wondered what it meant in the first place.

He ran down the levee slope and walked through the garden to the house. There he sat on the step, picking up bits of plaster and spilling them from one hand to the other.

He began to think of his marriage as he hadn't really thought of it before. He was a blundering fellow, all right. Maybe he shouldn't have married a girl like Victoria until he knew more about himself. His life had been all practical, hard practical problems of making White Cloud pay for itself with a little over for fun. He hadn't gone deep into anything much, certainly not the question of marriage.

Still, he realized, he had always had some pretty high ideas and ideals about it. No more playing around—and he'd done plenty of that, hadn't he? At Tulane, and then afterward. But now——

He'd wanted Victoria when he first saw her. She wasn't like anybody he had ever known.

The honeymoon . . . that had been pretty difficult. He guessed he just hadn't thought . . .

. . . hates having a baby, *or hates something about it* . . .

Lord! If he could just *talk* to Victoria, but he couldn't. Some things you just *couldn't* talk to her about. He didn't know, but maybe all nice girls were slow about waking up. Thunderation, it was idiotic to be ignorant in this way. He wouldn't wish anyone to know how unworldly he really was. Good God—people would laugh at him.

His musing switched suddenly to Flora. A spasm of feeling cut through his hazy, undirected reverie. He remembered in a vivid flash that evening at Fairfield when he had said good night to her, how her lips had parted under his kiss. Little Flora! Good Lord!

He tried to check the headlong rush of his imagination. What would it have been like if—if Flora—Flora with her arms about his neck? He groaned and struck savagely at his face, but the tears came suddenly, violently, and with them the sound of a lonely man crying.

The empty gallery of Far Félice echoed the sound.

Niles went more than once to Far Félice that dark December. He felt himself drawn to the ruined house. More than ever before in his whole life he thought consciously of the Grandolet family and its lively past. Stories of this and that ancestor came back to him, and gradually many of those who had been nothing more than shadows behind their names came variously to life. He wondered about Quintin, who was killed there that smothering, stormy day in July so long ago. The thought of the desperation, the ensuing terror, the cold horror following.

What kind of people were these, anyway? It was difficult to realize that it was his own ancestral flesh and blood which had flared into hate and murder.

He was curious, too, about Hippolyte d'Aupais, that handsome, winning scapegrace whose portrait had so engaged Victoria's fancy. There was plenty of legend, but not too much of factual story to go on. There was more to read in Hippolyte's face than in the letters and diaries of those who mentioned him, more to be learned from the insouciant smile and daring manner caught on canvas by a forgotten painter than in all the variations played on gossipy afternoons by Aunt Lucie and Cousin Marie.

The portrait said much, but here at Far Félice Niles was reading something more. He hadn't actually thought so much of these old houses as furnishing any light on the fading past. Of course there was always talk of the nobility of White Cloud. Yes, but something must be due the architects, he had thought. It was only lately that Victoria had discovered drawings of White Cloud which Quintin had submitted to the architects. So maybe, after all, the old Grandolets did have something to do with expressing themselves in their houses. But he had been still more interested when he saw that these drawings were a modification of some done by Hippolyte. *That* was why White Cloud was unlike any other Louisiana house he had seen, and that must explain Far Félice as well. There was no report on this point, but as Niles stood before the old house he realized that it had some of the same lightness that characterized White Cloud. It was a Latin quality, he decided.

Hippolyte seduced nice young girls of good family, he ran away from trouble, he wasted money and time, he apparently cared not a hoot for all the family's carefully built code and tradition—and yet he carried that happy face through life.

Perhaps it was Niles' own heritage from Isabella Niles and her stiff-necked ways that made him question the justice and propriety of this.

Saints alive, but wasn't he thinking exactly like a Puritan? And who had ever accused a Grandolet of *that*?

Niles was coming to know Far Félice as he had never known it. So many days he sat on the levee studying the pure flow of lines, the lovely grace and airy lift of the façade, the delicate balance—broken by the burned and fallen north section, the quiet patrician accent of the whole structure.

Niles felt himself inadequate as a thinker. He could only open himself to impressions, sense his emotional responses, and give himself to dreams. But he was sure, as he came time and again to this lonely and forgotten house, that something came into him from it—something in a language he could not understand but whose substance might become in some way a part of his own substance.

If Hippolyte d'Aupais spoke at all to his descendants it was from this house. White Cloud might go on and on repeating its story of grace and beauty, of aspiration and fidelity, but here he was reading another story. Niles felt that he was not intelligent enough to grasp it, not wise enough to understand it, not experienced enough to interpret it.

Hippolyte had left nothing—nothing but a pied and baffling legend, and this house. There was not a letter, nor a book, not a scrap of writing. There was, of course, that enigmatic inscription on the cornerstone of Far Félice. Niles had found it only recently: *Absit invidia.*

Was Hippolyte offering forgiveness to his family, or was he asking it for himself, or was he offering a light and happy philosophy to whosoever might pass by? *No ill-will.* Good enough. No one bore him any. The stories of his misdeeds were told with intent purpose, not only free of ill-will, but glossed with an oblique admiration.

Niles shrugged. The inconsistency of man!

He stared, now half seeing, now intently, at the blind face of Far Félice. He hypnotized himself into a communion with the builder.

. . . If Hippolyte d'Aupais said anything in this work of his mind and hand, he was saying that always he had been clear with himself. He knew the names of his own qualities and he said them aloud. He must have been incapable of hiding from himself.

Was that a quality of his century, maybe? And was this cloudy indecision and shadowy-mindedness characteristic of our own?

Niles turned away from the house to gaze at the river, dark and brown, lying like a curving arm about the whole of Far Félice. He looked back again past the house to the encroaching wilderness of swamp and close-ranked trees. The black land seemed to crouch.

He felt as he stood here that he was himself a symbol of this region. Lonely, troubled, wondering how to order his life, how to go on, how to make a living, even. There had been a glad life here once. It had been gay with people and sound. He was now the solitary watcher of the scene. In all the view not a single light showed, not a voice broke the winter stillness, not a sign of life moved anywhere.

Flamboyant and fancy musing, he said to himself with a gesture of brushing it all aside. The grandeur that was Rome, eh? I'm thinking like Aunt Lucie, and that arrives exactly nowhere.

Victoria felt better after the New Year, but she still spent much time in her rooms. She had fallen into a drowsy, moody state of mind, often not sure when she caught herself whether she had been sleeping or daydreaming. She drew deeper into herself and spent long days going over and over the factors and details of her new life here at White Cloud. She was like an embroiderer who fingers and sorts a tangle of many-colored silks, pausing again and again to plan the design and to contemplate the whole.

"Ever'body feels this way, Miss Victoria." Orlou dropped logs on the smoldering fire and brushed the bits of bark from her apron.

"How do you think I feel, Orlou?"

"I know. I know. Kinda uncertain and wondering."

"Well, that's certainly part of it."

"Yes, ma'am. You know, Miss Victoria, there's one thing about living 'way off like this in a lonesome place like White Cloud that maybe you didn't think about yet."

"What is that, Orlou? There seems a great deal I have still to think of."

"Yes'm. What I mean is being sure in your mind about what is and what's not."

Victoria blinked. "Do you mean what's real and what's not real?"

"Maybe so. But you know how it is, here we are away off, like I said. Weeks at a time there's nobody comes near the house. Wintertime, 'specially, when the roads are bad."

"I don't miss people—particularly since I don't know anyone here."

"You'll know ever'body after a while. Well, by and by, you get things all set wrong in your mind, you don't know which is big and which is little."

"Orlou, people talk like that in cities. They're always wanting to get away so they can get what they call a perspective on things. Do you understand?"

"Yes, ma'am. *Cela borne la vue—la perspective.*"

"Yes, and they wish always to go to the country so that they can do it."

"I think that's wrong, ma'am. When you have people around you, you can always measure things by them. Out in the country like this you get fooled. Time is a lot longer in the country."

"Sometimes it seems so."

"It *is*. It *is* so, indeed. Out here you have to measure things up against a great big sky, against the woods, or against the river itself. It's not human, and you forget how to think like a human."

"Unique philosophy, Orlou."

"No, ma'am. People like us colored people know that. I guess that's why we're always getting together for one thing and another. I tell you, Miss Victoria, you can just think and dream yourself out of this world. First thing you don't know what is what or what's alive and what is dead."

"Maybe you are right, I don't know. But I think I'll go downstairs. Is there a fire in my sitting room?"

"Yes, ma'am. Miss Lucie ordered it kept all the time for you."

Victoria leaned her face against the bedpost and steadied herself.

"Feel sick again, Miss Victoria?"

"Yes, oh, yes."

"Well, just rest against me a little."

At the head of the stairs, Victoria waited a moment. Then she retraced her step to the first column.

"What is it, Miss?"

"Come here, Orlou."

"Yes, ma'am."

"Listen."

"What is it, Miss Victoria?"

"Don't you hear anything here—right here at this place?"

"No, ma'am."

"Oh, yes you can, if you'll listen!"

"What does it sound like?"

"Whispers."

"Ma'am?"

"Oh, you think I'm out of my head. I'm not. I noticed it a long time ago. At this one spot when you listen the whole house seems to be whispering."

"That might be, but——"

"You agree then, it's possible."

"Lots of things are possible in an old house where so much has happened. There's been living and dying and birthing, and long-time crying, Miss Victoria."

"That's it, Orlou. It's nothing supernatural, but maybe something we don't understand yet. Maybe the old house is trying to tell me something. Do you hear it now, Orlou?"

Orlou's face did not change expression. "Yes, ma'am," she said quietly.

"You do, really?"

"Yes, ma'am. But I've always known about it. So has Miss Lucie."

"And Niles?"

"Nobody ever mentioned it to him. He's never said anything. But I guess he knows about it. Come along, Miss, you'll get chilled out here in the gallery."

They met Niles on the stair.

"Going to your Isabella room, honey?"

"Yes."

"Mind if I come along?"

"Of course not."

The room was warm and cheerful. Niles shifted the magazines on the table. "Like me to read to you?"

"I think not, thanks."

"Anything I can do?"

"No, not a thing."

"Gee, honey, I'm sorry you feel so bad."

"Let's don't talk about it. It's all right."

"Well——"

"Let's don't talk for a while. I just want to sit here."

"Shall I go?"

"No."

Victoria did wish to talk to Niles, but she did not quite know how to begin. Niles was still a stranger. Maybe in his practical way he might know the answers to small vexatious speculations. She wondered. What was Niles really like? What did White Cloud really mean to him, for instance? Was he just proud of a fine old place that was sometimes too eloquent a reminder of vanished glories? Or was he aware of the many possible effects it could have on people? Was Niles clear about "what is what or what is alive and what is dead," as Orlou said?

Certainly, she admitted, *she* was not clear—she was less and less clear about many things which lay there at the border of what was and what possibly was not.

Maybe she was always to be pretty much alone in her reaction to this house and its past—now her house, and the past, too, inextricably a part of her present and her future.

The fire fluttered and hummed and burned to a deep glow.

The dusk darkened the windows, and a small sound whimpered in the chimney.

Victoria stared at the fire. Niles sat quiet in a wing chair that shielded him from the glow of the fire. His face was in the shadow. Victoria could not see that he was watching her, studying her white immobile features, puzzling, and tormenting his brain about her.

He was thinking again of the afternoon in the gallery of Far Félice. What kind of small crisis had that been which brought the unaccustomed tears to his eyes and struck at him with the very gesture of despair? What now? He demanded an answer of himself.

Shifting a little in his chair he considered Victoria. There, sitting there by the fire this quiet afternoon, was his wife. Now: what he wished to know, definitely and clearly of himself, was if in his heart he was in love with Flora.

A tingling sense of guilt went slowly over him. He was enveloped in it, and it burned painfully against every resistance his mind set up against it.

Was he in love with Flora?

He had known her always. He had played with her, kissed her, cousin fashion, held her in tenderness and whimsical affection. Yes, but now? Now that Flora was no longer a child, and the senses of both of them were wide awake and singing —what now? What, indeed?

Niles bit his lower lip to keep it from trembling.

Something had come about, somehow, while he was unaware of it. Yes, he had today to say to himself that Flora was something new to him, something utterly enchanting and delicious. He was thrilling to the thought of her. Yes, he knew well the symptoms and the presence of passion in his blood. This was it.

There had been times when he was wholly other than he now was, and with women wholly other than Flora, when this keen edge of danger had been an intoxication. What had happened to him that he turned away from desire and the exhilaration of desire as from utter peril?

There was madness in him today, he thought, and in him, too, was a sane man who must live with that madness.

Flora? There was a story in the family of a Grandolet and a Vélazy who had defied everything and everybody.

He felt all at once like a young boy. Into his sharpened awareness came a resurgence of an old innocence that burned like fire upon his consciousness.

Maybe, he thought, maybe he was old-fashioned that in this moment he remembered the words of his marriage vows, spoken honestly to Victoria's father.

The color and the feel of romance flowed back again across his mind, obliterating a momentary cynicism, stilling the boisterous debate his senses were all ready to launch, drawing a curtain against a too-certain lure, shutting himself into an unworldly twilight of the spirit.

Victoria had almost forgotten Niles' presence, but thinking of him now in the tense stillness of the closed room, she felt beyond doubt that Niles, too, was away on a voyage of his fancy.

She recalled Orlou's comments of the afternoon. It was true. One did not have anything against which the imaginings of the mind might be measured. Was Niles running away, and far, in his dreaming?

How strange it was that she, Victoria, from another world of ideas and feelings, should be sitting here, spinning all of her future out of the fragments of a past she scarcely knew, and which in its essence she knew she did not understand at all. She did not understand it in the sense that she could re-create it, but she understood its powers well enough to use them. For she had decided that she *would* use them.

She was angry that she was so ill. A sense of deep humiliation thrust at her. She felt *used,* horribly, dreadfully used.

This child—it must be a son, it must be. If it was, she would never have another. Niles could do as he pleased. She would not question, or care. Anything rather than this—this unbearable violation. But—if it should not be a son she would have to go on. White Cloud must have a son, her son. There must be a Grandolet, her own Grandolet son.

From where she sat she could see the portraits. Isabella Niles looked out, steady and grim. You can have what you wish, she seemed to say, you can do whatever you wish. All of that is no more than the challenge to your strength. If you don't waver, and don't weaken, you can do anything.

You can do anything.

Hippolyte's face danced in the flicker of a small flame that sputtered for a moment at the edge of a log. Yes! I lied and I cheated, and I ran away. But I came back. I had everything I wanted.

I had everything I wanted.

Niles stirred in his chair. "Asleep, Vicky?"

"No. I thought you were."

"I was just thinking."

"So was I."

He arose and dropped another log on the fire.

"Niles."

"Yes, honey."

Victoria's quick ear caught a change in his tone. It was new.

Something patient, gentle, a little far away—and impersonal.

"Yes, honey. What is it?"

"Who are the richest people in this region?"

"Oh, goodness, I don't know. You mean planters?"

"Yes."

"Well, maybe the Alexanders, or the Dupres. I don't know. Why?"

"Just wondered. Why are they?"

"Why are they rich?"

"Yes, of course."

"Partly luck. Good land and lots of it. Brains."

"Who are the Alexanders?"

"Old family."

"Are they related to you?"

"Very distantly, maybe. Marriage connections."

"I don't see how you keep your relations straight."

"You know what Flora says?"

"No."

"Kinfolks are kissing kin. When they get too distant or too tacky, you stop kissing and they aren't kinfolks any more."

"Oh! Sounds like Flora, doesn't it?"

"Why were you asking about the Alexanders?"

"I wasn't. I was asking who is rich, and why?"

"Why do you want to know?"

"I'm curious as to why some people, side by side with others, have money, and some have not."

"I thought you were not interested in money."

"I'm not—not for myself."

"Then——"

"We're going to have a son. There'll be a Grandolet family to go on and on. White Cloud shouldn't go down."

Niles flushed. "All that is easier said than done, Vicky."

"I'm not critical, Niles. I'm not looking back at anything. I'm looking ahead."

"You sound so New England!"

"We don't have to be Southern in any poor sense of the word, do we?"

"We are not, and never have been."

"Oh, don't be touchy."

"I know what you mean. I understand it far better than you do. Most of us walk backward into the future. That's what's the matter with us."

"I believe it is." Victoria spoke thoughtfully. "Niles, you said yourself we were just starting a new era down here. You should be in on it."

"And do what?"

"What about timber?"

"Northern interests have bought a lot, but there's a lot more."

"Why don't you buy ahead of them? Watch which direction they are going."

He laughed gaily. All of the moods of the afternoon were gone.

"Buy with what?"

"On credit. You must stand well."

"Oh, as far as that goes——"

"Couldn't—couldn't you bring Flora in?"

"Flora?"

"Yes. Her money and property, and your credit. You wouldn't be afraid, would you?"

"Not for myself. But I wouldn't want to risk Flora's property."

"Everyone has to risk."

"*She* doesn't have to."

She colored slightly. "I guess I *am* a New Englander. Niles, I see the Negroes drifting lazily about the place—all over the place. Wouldn't it be better to have some sort of industry for them to be really busy at all of the time?"

"Now, honey. A lot of people think so. We just hate to be ambitious, you know. It takes so darned much energy."

"You work hard."

He sobered for a moment. "Harder than most."

"Let's plan, Niles. Let's make White Cloud great again."

"Oh, Lord, Vicky. Something in that makes me think of Isabella Niles."

"I rather think I like Isabella. From what I can learn she had what we in New England call gumption."

"Also git-up-and-git."

Victoria smiled. "That's too——"

"But with Isabella, I think it was git somebody else up and git 'em to work."

"I still like her."

"Well, well, I think I like Hippolyte better. Anyway, I'm sure he had a better time."

"He apparently took whatever he wanted."

Niles looked hard at the smiling portrait. "Yes, he took what he wanted. I wonder if it made any difference after a hundred years? *Does* it make any difference now to anyone?"

"Little enough, I imagine." Victoria had arisen and was smiling unconsciously in response to the inviting smile of Hippolyte.

"All we do is smile at him, indulgently, and say inside of us, that's the boy! I hope you had a good time—there isn't even a bone of you left now, up there in your tomb at Far Félice."

"Ugh! Niles——"

"Sorry, Vick. You get a kind of fatalism here sometimes.

You *feel* time go by. There's such a sense of yesterday and the days and days before yesterday—all the rows and rows of nice usable days stretching back to the same place, those little bricked-up graves at Far Félice."

"You're being a little morbid, aren't you?"

"No." He spoke shortly. "Just realistic."

"I think I'll go back upstairs."

"You're feeling better, aren't you, just now?"

"Yes."

"Fine."

"I had something else to think about."

He stopped at the door. "You know, Vicky——"

"What, Niles?"

"Maybe those weren't such bad ideas of yours, after all."

She took his arm. "Think about it, anyway."

"I'm going to."

Upstairs she paused as they rounded the gallery, and turned her head to one side as if listening.

"What's the matter, Vicky?" Niles looked at her anxiously.

"Nothing. Nothing at all."

NINE

FLORA CAME OFTEN to White Cloud with John Connor. It was privately agreed among the Grandolets and among a few intimate friends that John was a surprising husband for Flora. Unsuitable: that was Aunt Lucie's mild but final condemnation. No one was quite specific about just what qualities made him an unsuitable husband and, consequently, a regrettable addition to the ranks of "kissing kin." Victoria, within herself, agreed, but on clear grounds. Flora was fanciful, gay, witty, and as much of Louisiana's old order as if she had been born half a century earlier. She was completely what the Grandolets defined as "a lady." Again Victoria agreed. Flora, like so many of her kind with her special training and tradition, seemed much more trivial and thoughtless than she was.

"Flora's a sort of durable butterfly," Niles said.

"What about John?" Vicky asked him one day.

"Well, John—oh, John's all right."

"By which you mean he isn't."

"I don't know how you figure that out."

"All of you have exactly the same opinion of John Connor, Niles. There's so much faint praise of him."

Niles grinned. "He has a wonderful lot of good points."

"What do you find missing?"

"Well—well, now—nothing I can think of, really."

"But Aunt Lucie said 'unsuitable.'"

"He's a kind of stranger."

"But——"

"He's a stranger to our ways, Victoria."

"So am I!"

"Not fundamentally. You *get* things. Now, John—he's good, I think, nothing of the rambunctious, hell-bent ways, say, of Flora's brother Louis——"

"But you'd have thought someone just like Louis would have been more suitable?"

"We'd have understood such a person more easily."

"Someone like Hippolyte d'Aupais."

"Even someone like Hippolyte, yes. I know it doesn't seem to make very good sense, Victoria, but—that's the way we work inside, that's the way we are."

"John is good-looking——"

"And steady——"

"And he's devoted to Flora——"

"And he'll make a good husband——"

"And isn't he tiresome?" Victoria laughed merrily. Niles hadn't heard her laugh like that in a long time.

"You see, Vicky? You're just like us."

"I'm honestly a little sorry for Flora, Niles. She likes fun."

Niles shrugged and made a Gallic gesture which said, *There it is, what can you do about it?* He followed the gesture with a lift of his eyebrows, another lesser shrug, and a quick sideway tilt of his head—a whole sequence of comment without words.

"John likes to go fishing," he added irrelevantly, and again Victoria laughed.

Victoria spent many days in bed. The winter months

dragged by. There were visitors, but she seldom felt well enough to see anyone. Flora came, smiling, sympathetic, tender, and a little shy. Once in a while John came with her. Niles was quick to see that he irritated Victoria and was tactful in keeping him out of her range.

"What a house!" he said one afternoon while Niles was out of the room.

"Yes, it is, isn't it?" Victoria answered as gently as she could.

"You know what I'd do if I was Niles?"

"What?"

"I'd tear about two thirds of it down and get it out of the way."

"Oh, John!"

"Sure, that's what I'd do."

"I can't imagine——"

"Yes, I know. Old family stuff, but look, Victoria. All those old slave quarters on the court back there—perfectly useless. Takes a lot of repairs and the like to keep 'em from falling down."

"Well, they're part of the general design, I guess."

"Maybe, maybe. I don't know about all that kind of stuff. I'm practical. And then there are the two wings——"

"You aren't going to suggest tearing *them* down, are you?"

"That's exactly what I'd do. Perfectly useless nowadays. Gosh, how many rooms are there in this old place?"

"About seventy."

"Seventy! Think of it! Seventy rooms and four people!"

"I think White Cloud would look rather strange with its two wings gone."

"It'd look all right, Victoria. You'd still have a lot more room than you need, and cut down expenses, too. I expect Niles could do with a little saving here and there."

"I don't imagine——"

"You know what Niles told me today?"

"What?"

"That north wing hasn't been used since the war! And two years ago they spent five hundred dollars fixing the roof and repairing the damage from some leaks they didn't even know about. I think that's a blame-fool way to do."

"John, I guess we don't know exactly what these old houses mean to families that have lived in them so long."

He slapped his knee resoundingly. "That's just it! You hit the nail on the head there. They're not practical, not up to date about such things. Now, you take Wyandotte; it's not a third as big as White Cloud, but do you know what I'd like to do?"

"I'm afraid I do."

"I'd take it down and build a small, practical, up-to-the-minute modern house that would be comfortable. Just as we did at Rennover."

"I hadn't heard about that."

"Oh, Lord! Did that raise a rumpus! The house was a great big barn of a place—just like White Cloud—ornamental as a Christmas tree, and with the doggonedest lot of formal garden you ever saw. *Acres* of the blame stuff. We tore the house down—had a job getting it down, too—and dug up all that hedge stuff, and planted it in grass. It was pretty as a picture when we got it finished. Neat."

Victoria made an unintelligible response.

"But you ought to have heard the Rennovers carry on! We bought it from them, you know."

"I can understand——"

"Hell, Victoria, they sold it, didn't they?"

From that day Victoria used John Connor as the target of a consistent campaign of malicious wit. Whenever possible she led him into traps, encouraged him to enlarge upon his ideas, and conspired in the exposure of his amazing obtuseness.

John Connor was, as Flora had said at first, extraordinarily good-looking. One expected a vivacious and witty Irish mind to be at attention behind his good-humored blue eyes. But always Victoria baited him before others, held him up to devastating revelation of clumsy thickness and an intellectual ineptness that was wholly embarrassing. Niles tried often to head her off, and Aunt Lucie wavered protectingly between the two. Poor Flora watched this recurring shame with a horrid mixture of emotion. John, poor John, he was hers, but how, how, how could he think like that and, worse, talk like that?

Flora was sorry for him sometimes and tried to shield him. She could be furious with Victoria at the same time she was sickeningly aware of the bitter truth that was progressively apparent.

Sometimes she left the room, abandoning John to his fate. It was useless, she had already discovered, to waste her sympathy; he was actually unaware of what was happening.

Aunt Lucie found her more than once flung across the big bed, her face flaming, and hot tears in her eyes.

"Oh, Aunt Lucie——"

"Yes, darling, I know, I know. I think perhaps I—or Niles—should speak to Victoria——"

"Oh, no, no, no, no!"

"But, my dear, Victoria is being a little cruel, I think. Not that it seems to bother John much, I must say."

"That's just it. He doesn't—he *can't* see—oh, oh!"

"Never mind, honey. John is a good man, and Victoria is being thoughtless."

Flora sat up. "Aunt Lucie, don't deceive yourself. I guess I know Victoria better than anyone does. She *isn't* being thoughtless—not at all."

"Oh, my dear——"

"She has an awfully cruel streak in her." Flora fell back again among the pillows. "Heaven knows, I can't say John doesn't deserve some of the sharp things she says. Aunt Lucie, *how* can he think like that? I didn't see it for a long time, but every time he is around Victoria——"

"Dear child, we don't, we can't all see alike. John is not altogether used to our ideas. I dare say we are much out of date."

"You and Niles and Mama—what you are and think never could be out of date."

"He's had a different upbringing."

"That's just it. Aunt Lucie, could I—could I, do you think— have made a terrible mistake?"

"Now, Flora, you must not talk like that."

"That's what Mama says, only——"

"Only what?"

"She says I've made my bed and——"

"Dear, your Mama is a little bit too sharp, too, sometimes."

"Well, I'm not as stupid as all of you think, Aunt Lucie."

"Darling, we love you, all of us. No one ever dreamed of thinking you were in the least stupid. How can you say such a thing?"

"No, you think I don't know, that I can't see. I know I've married a fool."

"Flora!"

"But I'm not sure that it was a mistake, even at that!"

Aunt Lucie tried not to laugh, but Flora sat up and looked

straight at the sweet old face. Then she laughed a little, wiped her eyes, and blew her nose vigorously.

"Shoot it all, anyway. I just had to get married, that's all."

"Why, what do you mean, Flora?"

Flora made a helpless gesture, still laughing, still crying. "Not what you're thinking, you naughty person."

"Well, well——"

"Niles." Flora dropped the name heavily.

"Honey, you don't mean——"

"Oh, you knew it! You must have. When I lost him, I had to fill my life with something—quick. I guess that's all there was to it. I—I kind of like John, though."

"Of course you do. You're just——"

"I'm not overwrought, and I'm not hysterical. I was head over heels in love with Niles when I was a little girl. I will always be in love with him. I'm not jealous. He has what he wants—Victoria is a wonderful girl, Aunt Lucie."

"Yes, dear, of course, but what a happiness it would have been!"

TEN

SIGNS OF SPRING ARRIVED. Winter at White Cloud seemed not to be a season at all, but a sort of interlude. There was no snow, no frost, no really gloomy day. There was only a brief waiting for another spring.

The sense of pause ceased, and the disturbing awareness of preparation and movement invaded everyone. The windows were open again and the air drifted languorously from the south. It was with a catch in her breath that Victoria saw one morning as she stood on the upper gallery the whole east bank of the river appear in a delicate mist of grayish green and pink. The evergreens which had seemed so brightly green until now looked dingy and dark. The magnolias made an untidy litter of their shining leaves, and presently long lines of yellow jasmine were threading the shrubbery. The garden was alive with birds in continuous motion.

The river, as she shaded her eyes and peered at it through the misty air, seemed to run faster. The sunlight flickering on its crisscross currents made a vivacious scherzo for the eye.

Spring, and she had still three months to wait. Victoria was both impatient and afraid.

Dr. Cheer came often, shook his head sympathetically over her periods of discomfort and sickness, tried to be jovial when she was able to be up, but left her nevertheless with an uneasy conviction that he was worried about her, and uncertain.

Victoria felt that she was the center of a circle of watchers, some of them kind, some of them indifferent, and—maybe outside of that immediate circle still others, the fateful ancient watchers of White Cloud. Were they friendly, or indifferent, or hostile? The massive bed in her room seemed the only secure island of safety in the entire house.

Downstairs Isabella Niles appeared pitiless, implacable even. She might well have been the author of Orlou's heavy phrase: "White Cloud—*c'est un endroit de la fécondité*. Things that don't bear on this place die." Yes, that was expected of her. That she must do.

Downstairs Hippolyte d'Aupais laughed in the shadows of his deep gold frame. In the lofty well the chandelier pulsed with light. On the gallery the house whispered. In this bed, the ancestral bed of the Grandolets, she imagined refuge from all the lurking suggestions of the house and its past. This had been the retreat of other women. They had had their ordeals, and they had survived.

"I suppose," she said one day to Orlou, "I suppose many Grandolets have died in this bed."

"No, ma'am."

"No? Why not?"

"Because, ma'am, the old Grandolets always move out and give these rooms and this furniture to the young ones."

"So no one dies here—in this particular bed?"

"No, ma'am."

"No one dies here," she repeated to herself softly.

"That bed, Miss Victoria—I guess you might say it's a place of life. Death don't have anything to do with it. No, ma'am."

Grandfather Julien made his way upstairs as often as Victoria could see him, and Aunt Lucie hovered about with a fluttering concern. Victoria was not comfortable with anyone but Orlou. Niles felt this and made his visits to the room short.

For the first time in her life Victoria knew the need of someone to talk to. It was odd, she thought, that the one suitable someone was certainly Orlou. But even this need of communication did not go beyond a sort of verbal reaching out in the dark to touch a living presence. Her brain was blurred with sedatives, but it was heavy and shot through with near hallucinations. She felt herself retreat from monstrous imaginings, and knew most of the time that she was keeping out of reach of the distorted fancies which arose and swept toward her like a wave. She, Victoria, was still the spectator of her own nervous and psychic disturbance, and she held with every fiber of her strength to that clear dominion.

So April and part of May wore slowly away.

Niles came in late one evening. She noted absently that he held a yellow envelope in his hand.

"How is it going, Vicky?"

"Well enough, I guess."

"Gee, I'm sorry you're having such a bad time."

"It's all right."

"Anything I can do?"

"Of course not."

"Vicky."

Something in his tone aroused her. "Yes, Niles, what— is it?"

"I have to talk to you about something."

"What? What is it?"

"Do you mind being upset, honey? I don't quite know what to do. I have to talk to you, I guess."

"For goodness' sake——"

"It's just this." He tapped the telegram he was carrying. "It's your father."

"What's happened?"

"He is very ill."

"Oh!"

"It looks like I'd better go up there."

"Oh, Niles——"

"*You* can't go. He's all alone."

"I hate to have you go."

"I know, but——"

"He has so many friends—his parishioners——"

"But we can't let him die without someone from here——"

"Is he going to die?"

"Yes. It seems so."

Victoria closed her eyes. She did not wish Niles to see what was there. She was not surprised that this news brought no feeling of grief. Her foster father already seemed to have slipped far and far back into an unreachable past. It was almost startling to realize that he was actually alive. But it was not that which sent a quiver of dismay through and through her every nerve. It was the thought of Niles—alone with Dr. Dunstan. What deathbed confidence or confession might come about? Arthur Dunstan had, perhaps, ideas and codes of what he might call the right thing to do under such circumstances. What if—— No, no, no! That must not, must not happen.

She opened her eyes and smiled faintly at Niles. He touched her hand and her fingers closed tightly over his.

"What is it, Vicky? You want to say——"

"I'm sorry, of course, but—but, Niles——"

"Yes?"

She made up her mind. Niles must not go. The risk was too great.

"Niles—it's about time, you know."

"Yes, I know."

"I want you here."

"But—one way or another—I'll be back before then. It's two weeks, anyway. If your father dies, or if he is better—you see, I'll be back before two weeks——"

"No, no! Please——"

"All right, all right, dear. Don't disturb yourself about it."

Orlou came to the door. "Mr. Niles, someone wants to see you downstairs."

"I'll be right down. Don't worry about your father, Vicky. I'll telegraph tonight and get details."

Two days later Victoria was both furious and terrified to find that Niles had gone to New Hampshire. Furious that he had gone to Dr. Dunstan, to *her* home, without consulting her, treating her as if she were a child, terrified of what might come of the visit.

She had settled so many things in her own mind, she had begun to define her own place to herself, she was beginning to guess at the path that Isabella Niles had blazed, a pathway whose traces remained clearly enough for one who could read the signs. She had even guessed the far-future dangers of Flora, and to shape her own strategies to meet whatever might come from that not easily predictable source.

And now. Everything hung precariously in balance. A word from Dr. Dunstan under the automatic action of what he called his conscience and the innate demands of honesty might ruin everything. Again—she weighed Niles and his character carefully, thoughtfully—again nothing might be lost. Niles had a strange and unfathomable sense of honor. Possibly, just possibly, nothing might happen, even if Dr. Dunstan forgot his promise to her. But inwardly her position would be changed. She would have to walk humbly, gratefully even. No, no, no, no! *It must not happen.*

She could not sleep. Her wretched sickness increased.

A week passed and there was no word from Niles. Of course it would take him four days to reach Glaston, and four more days for a letter to come. But why didn't he telegraph? That meant Dr. Dunstan was living. That was the real danger, of course. If only he had died before Niles reached him.

Late at night she heard Aunt Lucie and Orlou talking outside of her door.

"I can't feel that I should tell her now," Aunt Lucie was saying.

Victoria's heart jumped, and all of her senses sprang wildly to attention.

"I don't know what to say, Miss Lucie. She hasn't slept, hardly a-tall."

"Maybe she is in such suspense. It might be best to tell her. I—I just don't know."

"It's hard to say."

"I guess, anyway, I'll wait until morning and ask Dr. Cheer."

Victoria sagged wearily against her piled-up pillows.

"Aunt Lucie!"

The door opened. "Yes, Victoria?"

"I heard you——"

"Oh——"

"Tell me."

"My dear child——"

"Don't speak that way. *Tell me.*"

"Well——"

"You've heard from Niles?"

"Yes, dear."

"Father is dead?"

"Y-yes, Victoria."

"When?"

"Before Niles reached him. I'm so sorry, dear."

"Why did Niles delay telegraphing, I wonder?"

"I suppose he didn't know whether you should be told or not."

"When did you hear?"

"Three days ago."

Victoria closed her eyes that Aunt Lucie might not see the cold rage she felt at this senseless, tormenting delay.

"We've had a telegraph message every day."

"Yes?" Victoria forced her voice to weakness. She wanted to shout, and scream, and drive Aunt Lucie from the room.

"The funeral was yesterday."

"When is Niles coming home?"

"He said there were some small matters to be straightened out. He asked if he had time. There are a lot of papers and things of that kind, I imagine."

"*Papers?*"

"Yes, dear. In every house——"

"Telegraph Niles not to trouble—to bring all papers and letters—*to me*. Will you send that right away, please?"

"Yes, of course. I understand you want Niles here, dear, and I'm sure——"

"Yes, yes, of course."

"My child, I'm very sorry we never knew your dear father. Flora says he was most charming."

"Yes, thank you. Orlou——"

"Yes'm."

"I want to sleep."

The next day Dr. Cheer came to White Cloud early without being sent for.

"Just had a feeling I'd better come around, Miss Lucie. How is she?"

"Depressed, and strange, Dr. Cheer. I declare I don't quite seem to understand Victoria."

The doctor looked noncommittal. "She's different from us. We're pretty provincial, I guess, Miss Lucie. Never have taken any trouble to understand other kinds of folks."

"I don't mean just that. She's *strange*, Doctor."

"Well, well, I'll run up and have a look."

He met Orlou on the stairs.

"Oh, I was just coming down to send for you, Dr. Cheer."

"Beginning, eh?"

"Yes, sir."

The following morning, Dr. Cheer came downstairs, haggard and disheveled.

"Miss Lucie!"

"Yes, Doctor, yes. What is it?"

"Send someone right off to the telegraph office. I'll have to have Dr. Chaussegros up from New Orleans, without delay."

"Right away, Doctor. I'll send Luther. Emsy, get some coffee for the doctor."

"Better telegraph Niles, too. Tell him—well, whatever is keeping him is a lot less important than this. He'd better hurry. I don't know what's going to happen."

"Yes, Doctor."

Dr. Cheer ate his breakfast abstractedly. Aunt Lucie sat opposite, her face knotted with anxiety.

"I don't understand it, Dr. Cheer. Victoria has always seemed to be such a healthy—such a normal girl."

"That's got nothing to do with it." He snapped the words out crossly. "All sorts of factors."

"I do wish Niles would come."

"Yes, so do I."

"Doctor, is there—any immediate danger?"

"Yes."

"She might die?" Aunt Lucie was very pale, and she whispered the words.

"Yes."

Upstairs Victoria lay crushed and torn under the ceaseless onslaught of an agony that seemed each moment more than she could bear. Her lips were bitten and swollen, her face blotched and almost unrecognizable. Now and then the cloudy confusion in her brain cleared for a moment. She held tight to Orlou's quieting hands. But in these fleeting moments of clarity Victoria knew that she was resolving herself into a new person. This—this unspeakable horror, this ultimate degradation, was setting her apart. She tried to think, but there was no time. She only knew that after this she would be—would be—she could not formulate just what, but even now she could draw some strength and fortitude from that vaguely looming something, that changed someone who would be the new Victoria Grandolet. A faint sense of that person came to her, someone cold and strong, enclosed and separate, someone set beyond the possibility of another such experience. This was making another person in the place of what she had been.

A kind of wild, animal rage possessed her. It was shot through with a frothing hate of all that brought her here— Niles, the child itself, the Grandolets, the house, the—the world.

She felt Orlou hold her arm tightly, the sligh prick of a needle.

A choking mist seemed to fill her throat, to cloud the room, to settle on her with nightmare weight. She heard Dr. Cheer say: "Dr. Chaussegros will be here by midnight."

The next morning Dr. Chaussegros called for Miss Lucie.

"Have you heard from Mr. Grandolet?"

"Just now."

"When will he be here?"

"He can't possibly reach White Cloud until tomorrow."

"We can't wait."

"What is it?"

"We'll have to take the responsibility of the decision ourselves. It is either Mrs. Grandolet or the child. We'll sacrifice the child."

Aunt Lucie pressed her hand to her throat. "I'm sure Niles would agree to this—instantly."

Dr. Chaussegros turned to Dr. Cheer. "I think we can risk waiting two or three hours. Do you agree?"

"Yes."

"Emsy!"

"Yes, Miss Lucie."

"Tell Father the doctors are having breakfast——"

"Just a hurried bite, Miss Lucie. I think Dr. Chaussegros would like to lie down first for an hour."

"Yes, thank you. And then——"

Orlou had come out in the hall and heard the last few words. She turned back into Victoria's room and quietly locked the door behind her.

Crossing the room, she stared hard into Victoria's unseeing

eyes. Carefully, she half raised the exhausted, moaning girl and held her tight.

"Miss Victoria!"

Only a smothered sound came in response.

"Miss Victoria! Miss Victoria!"

This time Victoria's eyes cleared a little.

"Can you hear me, Miss?"

"Yes."

"I want you to drink something."

Victoria shuddered.

"It'll taste bad, but you *must* drink it. Can you hear me? Will you try?"

"Yes." The reply was hardly more than a movement of the lips, but Orlou laid her back on the pillows. She quickly lighted a spirit lamp and set a small pan over the flame. Then she went to the door, opened it, and listened. She locked it again, made sure the doors in the adjoining room were also fastened, and returned to the bed.

"Miss! . . . Miss Victoria!"

A weak gesture of a hand answered.

"Drink this—quick, now."

Victoria shrank back a little.

"Drink it quick—and don't tell anybody I gave it to you."

Victoria opened her eyes. A question appeared.

It's bush medicine. Drink it——"

"What——"

"Colored people know some things, Miss. They have to have things to cure them. They don't have doctors."

Victoria whimpered feebly.

"Drink it, Miss. This is Orlou. I'll help you."

Slowly and with the greatest effort Victoria drank.

Orlou washed the cup and the pan with care. She sniffed

to be sure no odor remained in the room or on the cup. Then she unlocked the door, drew the shades against the light, and waited.

Two hours later the child was born. A son.

ELEVEN

THE GRANDOLETS SPENT the late summer at Lake Ponchartrain, returning to White Cloud early in October. Each member of the family felt change. Each felt it in a different way.

Grandfather Julien was quietly pleased that Victoria had named his great-grandson Julien Quintin. Niles called him Q-G, and the easy nickname came quickly into familiar use. Old Julien was not really well. Ancient malaria, lurking in his system, broke out actively. The fragile old gentleman crumpled visibly under attacks, and much of his crackling vitality and sharp talk were gone. He seemed to feel with the arrival of his great-grandson that he had already lived too long. He often said so, and Victoria alone could recall him to his accustomed self.

Everyone recognized that Julien's liking for Victoria stood back of her like a visible protection. That he was silently, but so militantly, protective was already an admission that she needed it. This attitude created an unexplainable watchfulness all around.

Aunt Lucie kept a look on her gentle face that was clearly uneasy, also a little questioning, as if something had happened to her and she still did not know what it was.

No one outside of the house knew that Niles had not returned to his rooms with Victoria. For the first time in many years the shutters of the north wing were open. No one, of course, dared ask a question, and the situation was ignored. What passed between Niles and Victoria no one even guessed. It was well after Thanksgiving when Flora first noticed the open shutters.

"Aunt Lucie, who in the world is in the old north wing?"

Aunt Lucie laid her fingers on her lips and presently Flora followed her upstairs. Aunt Lucie closed the door and stood leaning against it.

"Flora, you mustn't say anything about this, even to John."

"About what? I don't——"

"It's Niles."

"What's Niles? You don't mean he's——"

"I mean that he hasn't gone back to his old rooms—with Victoria."

"Why?"

"I don't know."

"Well, of course, there's the baby."

"Pinky takes care of the baby altogether."

"Yes, I know."

"Pinky stays in the little room back of the old dressing room."

"Well——"

"It probably doesn't mean anything, Flora, except it just—well, doesn't seem natural somehow."

Flora's face darkened. "If anything has happened——"

"What do you mean, Flora, now what *do* you mean?"

"As you say, it doesn't seem very friendly, does it?"

"I am so worried about it—at least, I *guess* I am. I'm not even sure I am worried, and if I am I'm not sure what about."

[155]

Flora laughed. "Oh, Aunt Lucie, that sounds exactly like you!"

"Well, it is me, honey."

"You're not being very frank, you old darling."

"I declare to you, Flora, I say the truth when I say I don't know what I'm talking about."

"We might be close to gossiping, dear."

"Oh, my child. This is *family*. I thought Niles was so much in love with Victoria."

"You say *was*. Isn't he?"

"I don't know."

"But you think there's a change?"

"Well, there he is, living in Cousin Etienne's old rooms."

"Oh, darn it all. I wish you weren't such a lady, Aunt Lucie."

"Why, Flora!"

"I mean it. You've got some sort of idea in your head and you won't talk about it. You've seen something, or guessed something."

"No, honey. Word of honor. I guess I ought not to say anything, especially to you."

"In heaven's name! Why?"

"Because you—you are so fond of Niles, and you might worry about him."

"What you are trying to say is that I'm in love with him. I am. I have always been. You're right about one thing, but I think I'd do more than worry."

"Oh, my dear, what could anyone do? If——"

"If what?"

Aunt Lucie blushed. "Well, this is just guesswork, of course. I mean if there *should* be some little temporary difference between them."

"I know Victoria very well, Aunt Lucie. I shouldn't be afraid to say anything to her I thought necessary."

"Now, listen, darling child. We're sitting up here just working ourselves up about nothing—nothing at all. We don't even know what we're talking about."

"I think we do."

"Flora."

"Yes, Aunt Lucie."

"Don't you say this to your mother, but do you know, I'm a little afraid of Victoria."

"*What?*"

"Yes, I am, and I don't know why."

"You, Lucie Grandolet—*you* afraid of anything or anybody —and in White Cloud?"

"I guess I shouldn't have said that. It isn't exactly that I'm *afraid*. But I'm a little uncomfortable."

"Why?"

"She looks at me."

Flora laughed, and as abruptly sobered. "I think you'd better come over and pay me a good long visit at Wyandotte."

"I couldn't do that."

"Why not?"

"I don't know how Victoria would manage without me."

"Quite well, I assure you. With Orlou and Emsy and Luther —White Cloud could run itself."

"And Father."

"He likes Victoria."

"All of us do, Flora."

"I don't."

"*Flora!*"

"I *don't.*"

"You must not say that! But, why *don't* you?"

"Oh, twenty reasons. But Victoria's my cousin, now, and she's Niles' wife, and she's the mother of little Q-G."

"Isn't he wonderful, Flora?"

"Yes, I suppose so."

Flora sat for a while thinking of what Aunt Lucie had said. It was very little, truly. Perhaps they didn't, as Aunt Lucie said, know really what they were talking about. The fact that they were talking at all, and like this, was, she decided, significant.

What had come about? It was still incredible to her that Victoria should be here at White Cloud and that she herself was merely a visitor.

She had liked Victoria well enough at school, but she had never thought of her in any closer relationship than as a school roommate. Victoria had always been aloof. The other girls said she posed. Did she? Flora asked herself. The question was not easy to answer. If one posed, one posed as something. Victoria seemed never to have pretended anything. Flora drew her clear childish brows together in an effort to think hard and be honest. It was going to be hard to be honest and fair. She had been stunned when Niles married Victoria. She had been stunned for a long time afterward. She had married hastily to help her out of her trance. In that she admitted ruefully she had certainly succeeded. It had been a long time before her nerves had reasserted themselves. Then, she thought, she had come out of her trance, and she had come out "wild in the face" as they used to say about her brother Louis' temperamental tantrums.

Victoria. Victoria. She pulled her scattering thoughts together. She must think about Victoria. To what purpose now?

Back to that question of pose again. No, she did not believe that Victoria had pretended anything at all. She always spoke of the simplicity and the skimpiness of rectory life in the small New Hampshire town, of her father's unworldly goodness and innocence. She rarely spoke of plans or ambitions.

A phrase of Aunt Lucie's kept sounding out again and again in this roil of emotional recollections. *She looks at me.* Again Flora laughed, and again she smothered the laugh. That was an old trick of Victoria's. She had had a cruel way of disposing of girls she disliked. Some of the girls hated her for it. But no one could ever quite say what it was that Victoria did. *She looked at them.*

Flora tried to remember. Yes, yes. *She looked at them.* She looked at them as from a great distance, or from a remote height, looked as a greatly superior person might look at the ungraceful gambols of an awkward child, or as an utterly knowing person might look even while ignoring the gaucheries of someone terribly inferior. Victoria seemed at such times to recall her thoughts as from afar to the trivial considerations of the moment.

Wasn't it Katherine Lucius who said: "She puts on and it makes me so darned mad because I can't tell what it is she's putting on!"

The worst of it was that Victoria could make a whole group of girls feel she was the only one who wasn't "putting on."

Here at White Cloud Flora had not seen anything of this. But what had taken place over there in those rooms that Niles could not, or would not, stay there? And what was going on in Victoria, anyway? What could she want that she didn't already have? And why couldn't she simply and naturally be a part of the family that certainly seemed ready enough to accept her without question?

It was curious, Flora thought, how difficult it was to imagine Victoria being Niles' wife—being anyone's wife, for that matter.

Flora nodded to herself. "That's just about it," she said. This business of being married—well, for all the silly and shrewd talk that went on among girls, it was more than a surprise, and more than a shock. And as for fun—well! But Victoria. And then Flora felt her cheeks burn, and she swung about in her chair so that she could not see herself in the mirror. She was suddenly thinking about Niles, thinking of Niles and Victoria, thinking of herself and John. Every nerve came clamorously alive. Every nerve made shock of the thought of John Connor. But at the thought of Niles—— Could this be she? she asked. For with a frankness that appalled her she realized that she could do no more than endure John Connor, and that she could endure John Connor only because she could think of Niles.

Victoria maybe—could there be someone else who haunted Victoria as Niles haunted her? She could not easily believe so. It was rather that the place of Victoria's heart was altogether empty and that Niles or anyone could be an unbearable intrusion.

Flora compressed her flowerlike little mouth as much as she could, looking like a puzzled cherub. She guessed in this moment of keen intuition that she had surmised correctly. And, corollary to this surmise, she had more than a premonition that someway, somehow, she would do something about it.

Throughout the winter Victoria busied herself with the accumulation of old letters and diaries and newspaper clippings that Grandfather Julien had amassed and saved. She amused the family with long-forgotten stories, with anecdotes, and with a running comment that set the Grandolet history in what seemed at first to be a pleasantly picturesque light.

"I had no idea we were so interesting, Victoria." Niles spoke lightly, but there was a possible undertone of irony in the remark. "Are you sure you aren't suppressing the dull parts?"

"There are some things to be suppressed, yes."

Niles looked serious. "Maybe you don't know how much all of us know that we don't talk about."

Aunt Lucie broke in. "Oh, I'm sure the long story of the Grandolets and all of our kinspeople is just about like the stories of other people."

Grandfather Julien shook his head. "Lucie, you *are* a Grandolet and you feel you have to be loyal, and supporting maybe. But I think we were unusual in many ways."

"Oh, yes, of course, Father—but not unusually bad, do you think so?"

Victoria leaned forward with a kind of short-breathed eagerness—a mannerism which had lately appeared. "It is the intensity of the Grandolets that's rather special, Aunt Lucie. The impress of the old members of the family is everywhere. Perhaps I feel it more than you do."

"Why should you?" Aunt Lucie's tone was slightly dry.

"I'm new to the place. You are used to White Cloud. I see and feel things—sometimes." She allowed her voice to trail softly on the last word. Her eyes looked away as if she were thinking of something she would not discuss.

"Oh, my dear, I'm sure there's nothing *mysterious* about us —or the house, either."

"Houses *are* mysterious—just of themselves."

"It's an imaginative thought," Aunt Lucie conceded.

"Oh, no, no. Something else. People live in a place, and die and go away, and something is left."

"Hants." Niles clipped the word.

Aunt Lucie laughed. "I thought at first you said 'rats.'"

"Rats, too," he added.

"Victoria, my dear, these old houses have stories that grow just because they are told over and over."

"Perhaps I'm thinking of something different, Aunt Lucie."

"It's like the whisper in the first gallery," Aunt Lucie went on imperturbably.

Victoria looked startled.

"Haven't you heard it, Victoria?"

Victoria nodded.

Niles laughed shortly. "Trust Orlou to tell about such stuff."

"I—I heard it myself."

"Echoes, Vicky."

"Do you think so, Niles?"

"What else could it be?"

She shook her head slightly.

"My dear Vicky, all spooks are materializations of whatever you are afraid of."

Grandfather Julien interrupted. "Where did you get that idea, Niles?"

"Just thought it up, Grandfather, all by myself."

"I'm delighted I have such brilliant children."

Victoria refused the light turn of the talk. "There are still more things——"

"I know what you are going to say, Vicky. 'There are more things in heaven and earth,' and so forth, meaning to say—well——"

"Meaning to say what, Niles?"

"That maybe some people can see, and some can't."

"Whatever is everybody talking about?" Aunt Lucie was bewildered.

Niles looked at her blandly. "This is what is known as *such interesting conversation.*" The snap in his voice was pronounced.

Victoria ignored the tone and the remark. Aunt Lucie bridged the awkward moment. "Of course, I know old houses are different, but it's the sense of the past, the knowledge that these places have seen so much of life——"

"And remember," Victoria said the words softly.

"Now, listen, Vick. Don't try to *tell* us about White Cloud."

This time she flushed. "I was rather trying to tell you about myself, Niles, and maybe something about you, too."

Grandfather Julien seemed to have been dreaming for a moment. He came back suddenly.

"*Tu n'auras point peur de ce qui effraie pendant la nuit . . . ni de la mortalité qui marche dans les tenebres——*"

"*Ni de la destruction que fait le degot en plain midi.*" Aunt Lucie finished the quotation with the air of having summoned the Church to the exorcism of evil spirits.

"I read a book a while ago." Niles looked serious. "Something about the demon of noonday—the idea came out of that same psalm—it's the thing that gets you in plain daylight when you're least suspecting it."

"Meaning just what, Niles?" Victoria was looking superior again.

"Meaning—well, Vicky, I'm not sure you'd understand—yet."

"I could try." Victoria's tone was so sarcastic that Aunt Lucie stared in surprise.

"All right. It's this, Vick. You can be hurt by only two things in this world, the things you love and the things you believe in. If you believe in——"

"Hants?"

"I wasn't going to say 'hants,' but the word would do. No, I was going to say that if you believe in the dark devisings of the mind—spirit, if you'd rather call it that—and that they have any power at all, then"—he grinned impishly—"the goblins'll get you someday."

"But suppose there are powers—left over from other lives?"

"Open the windows and air the rooms!"

Grandfather Julien had been listening. "I've wondered sometimes——"

"Now, Grandfather, don't tell me you believe in such things!"

"*La mortalité qui marche dans les tenebres——*"

"Such as what?" Niles sounded a little angry.

"*La destruction que fait le degot en plain midi.* Why do you suppose such terrors were mentioned if they didn't exist?"

"They're in the imagination."

"The imagination is real, Niles."

"Ah!" Victoria smiled, but not at anyone.

Niles grunted. "Two steps farther along that line and you are brother and one with the conjure doctor."

"The Negroes know things we don't know, Niles," Victoria said.

"Don't try to explain Negroes to me, Vicky. I know a lot of things they don't know, too."

"Dogs seem to feel things sometimes," Aunt Lucie said.

"Yes, yes." Victoria leaned forward in her chair again. "There have always been signs on every hand of another world, or at least——" She hesitated.

"Victoria!" Niles was still jeering.

"Yes."

"Did you ever notice that Orlou looks like one of the sorceresses, or something, painted by Michelangelo?"

She nodded. "Like the Cumaean sibyl."

"Oh, you *have* noticed it?"

"From the first."

"Well, don't take it seriously."

"I don't know what you mean."

"She used to fill me up with the spook stuff when I was a child. I never did get over it."

Grandfather Julien placed the tips of his fingers carefully together. "Orlou is an extraordinary woman. I should place a good deal of reliance on her intuitions."

"Tch! Grandfather, Orlou's intuition is a kind of primitive observation with—er—unconscious deductions. That's all."

"That's a good deal, my boy. Something we haven't got."

"I think all of this sounds a bit crazy." Niles was more than annoyed.

"It's like this, Niles." Victoria spoke quickly. "Something like this, maybe. In an old house where many people have lived, there must have been hates in the minds of many, and griefs, and terrors that were too great for the people who felt them. Something remains—an overplus, or something. Maybe hates that were so great that even death could not quiet or satisfy them. The old conflicts are suspended, or maybe go on. Such forces could even use living people as the instruments of their unfinished purposes."

"Oh, Victoria, my dear! I never did hear of any such thing. Hates! Why, my dear——"

"I don't suppose people record such things for others to read, Aunt Lucie."

Grandfather Julien arose. "I'm going back to read about minerals. They're quite restful. Better take a vacation from those old letters and all that trash, Victoria."

"Father, don't encourage Victoria to think——"

"There's a lot to what she says, Lucie. But I'm too old to think about it. I promise you when I'm a ghost I won't bother anybody at White Cloud. That is—if you are good."

Victoria arose and put her arm about the old man. She laughed with an air of understanding camaraderie that brought a quick look of annoyance to Aunt Lucie's face.

Victoria laughed gaily. "Oh, Grandfather, *do* come back. I'll miss you, and I think you'd make a wonderful ghost!"

Aunt Lucie dropped her fancywork in her lap. "My dear Victoria, I hardly think——"

"But listen, Grandfather, don't come to White Cloud. Come to Far Félice! Is it a rendezvous?"

The old man drew up his shoulders and shook off her arm. "Don't ever mention Far Félice to me," he said and went quickly from the room.

"Victoria, my child, don't you know you can't talk to Father about Far Félice?"

"I *have* talked to him about Far Félice many times."

"It makes him very restless."

"Why?"

Aunt Lucie shrugged. "Who knows?"

"You see? It's what I've been saying about old places. There is something always left over from the past. I think, Niles, I think I'll use Father's insurance money and start restoring Far Félice."

"You are going—why, Niles, what *is* Victoria talking about?" Aunt Lucie was round-eyed.

Niles shifted a bit uneasily in his chair. "Oh, I gave Far Félice to Vicky—a long time ago."

"Oh, I see. I didn't know that, of course."

"It will stay in the family, I promise you, Aunt Lucie."

"I was not supposing it could be otherwise, Victoria. You

misunderstand my surprise. I—I don't believe any of the Grandolet women have ever wished to own any of the places—separately."

"I have a fancy for the old house."

"Are you really going to try to fix it up, my dear? What for?"

"Well, I think I'd like to find out why Grandfather Julien doesn't wish to haunt it." Victoria laughed again, but Aunt Lucie bent her face low over her embroidery.

The sense of discord hung heavily in the room. Victoria realized, with a clear question in her mind, that she rather enjoyed the feeling. It touched her with a flicker of excitement. With an instant retrospective turn of her attention, she remembered many occasions at school when she had experienced the same tingling sensation of victory. With it always had come a sustaining assurance of strength. It had pleased her, she remembered, to set a roomful of girls into a state of undirected resentment. People were really such fools!

She arose presently and went to her rooms. On the way across the hall, up the stairs, and along the gallery she walked quickly with a light and buoyant step. It was an odd and stimulating mood that was upon her. She paused for a fleeting moment by the column where the whispers purred in the silence.

She lifted her head and looked back along the circle of old portraits, then down to the lower floor where the black and white marble squares reflected the shine of the lights and the shadows of the paired columns.

Was it, she wondered, as dramatic in appearance as it seemed to her? There had been a time when standing here looking at it, she had felt as if the play were really over as Niles had said, as if this were an empty and deserted stage to which no actor would ever return. Her feeling about it was very different now. Now she was thrilled with a new certainty that the curtain had just gone up, and that she was only waiting for her cue. Presently the play would begin.

Time was also—and it seemed impossibly long ago—when she could not make up her mind about her relationship to White Cloud. It had been so withdrawn, so remote from any interest in her, so noble and contained, so imperious in the impress of its own power and personality on all who might enter it. She knew now that this could never be again for her. No: she had somehow, without knowing how or when, entered deep into it. Now, instinctively, she knew how it had come to be, why it appeared as it did, and how it could be used. That was it! That was her new and exhilarating knowledge. During these months she had looked long and closely at Isabella Niles and with an equally close scrutiny at Hippolyte d'Aupais. Without being aware of it at any moment of time, she had entered into their joint and incongruous company. She could never again, she felt, be afraid of White Cloud. With the unexpected formulation of that thought she realized with a start that there had been a time, not so long ago, when she *was* afraid of it. Yes, *afraid* of it. But not now.

The surprising reaction downstairs to her mention of Far Félice gave her for the moment an assurance that she understood why she could not fear White Cloud. White Cloud had been a Grandolet escape from Far Félice—from whatever "dark devisings" had characterized, or cursed, that strange place, and—*Far Félice was her own*. It was as if she had stepped back through the decades into the grim and shadowy powers that had directed the ancient Grandolets, as if the mere abstraction of possession had invested her with all that Far Félice had been in its still unrevealed past.

She hummed softly as she went back through her rooms to the small corner room where Pinky cared for the baby.

"He's sleepin', ma'am."

Pinky stood aside and Victoria sat down beside the rosewood crib which Aunt Lucie had brought down from the attic. Q-G, as he was now generally called, was going to be dark. The Grandolet look was already clearly defined in the set of the eyes and the shape of the brows. A faint uneasiness ruffled Victoria's pleasurable state of mind. For an instant she had the sensation of an open door at her back, or an unexpected breath of east wind on her neck.

She had thought more than once since her baby had been born of unforeseeable heredities. She had shaken the intrusive disquiet aside. There was not, she felt, anything in herself to give ground to fears. And how many unknown factors lay potential in the multiple variety of Grandolet inheritances? She could forget all that had gone before, her acute shrinking from the marriage bed, her body, racked and nearly destroyed in the fathomless agony of childbirth—she could put all of that away from her.

The door opened and Orlou came in. "Oh, I didn't know anyone was here, Miss Victoria. I saw Pinky in the hall outside. I thought maybe Q-G was alone."

"No."

"Isn't he the prettiest baby you ever saw, Miss?"

"I've seen very few babies, Orlou."

"Well, he certainly is pretty."

"He does look like his father, doesn't he?"

"Yes, ma'am. He's all Grandolet."

"Well, Orlou." Victoria smiled. "I hope he's a little bit me, too."

"Yes'm. But it's nice and it's right for a boy to look like his pa."

"I suppose so."

"Ain't you mighty proud?"

"Yes, Orlou."

"I hope you have a big family, Miss."

"Oh, no, no, no, Orlou!"

"Why not, Miss? Think of a whole lot of fine Grandolet boys."

Victoria's face went haggard. She appeared so stricken that Orlou looked narrowly at her.

"What's the matter, Miss Victoria?"

"Nothing, Orlou. Nothing."

"It's natural, Miss Victoria, to have children."

Victoria turned away abruptly.

Victoria had never, even to her inmost consciousness, come out into the open in plain view of herself. She was thinking of that now as she tried to define Orlou's enigmatic expression. It was strange, she thought, that she could not easily say which was herself, the self she was now observing—a self that was going into action—or the self that was observing. Here was a self, or a part of herself, which was proceeding coldly and ruthlessly. There was another that looked on. But she was also aware of yet something else, or some yet farther self, detached, coolly weighing the possible outcomes. It was like two mirrors, facing each other, multiplying an image again and again, each one half hiding behind another, away and away into a twilit limbo where features and character were indistinguishable and lost. Was there any such person, she asked, as Victoria Grando-let? It was all so teasing and uncomfortable.

Orlou came in again to light the lamps. A few minutes later

Niles came in through the bedroom. She looked up in surprise.

"Oh, it's you!"

"Yes. Surprised?"

"Startled. I didn't hear you."

"Just went in to see Q-G."

"He's sleeping."

"Yes."

Victoria took the hairpins from her coiled hair. Orlou picked up the brush.

"Never mind, I'll brush it."

"Yes, ma'am." Orlou disappeared quietly.

Victoria brushed slowly and carefully, absently regarding herself in the mirror.

"Lord, but you are beautiful, Vicky."

She smiled one-sidedly and shrugged slightly. Niles arose, drew her hair back from her face, and kissed her on the cheek. She held quite still. He sat down beside her on the bench and put his arm around her. She neither avoided nor returned his kisses.

"What's the matter, Vick?"

"Nothing. Why?"

"You're not exactly responsive, you know."

"Oh." The word was light and disdainful.

"Well, you know there's nothing reprehensible about a little affection."

She laid the brush back on the dresser and dropped her hands in her lap.

"Is there anything wrong with me, Vick?"

"I don't know what you are talking about, Niles."

"Oh, yes, you do. We happened on this once before. I—I guess I was impatient."

"I'd rather not talk about it."

"Well, I *want* to talk about it."

"*Must* you?"

"Yes."

"Niles, don't you know how I feel about—all that sort of thing?"

"For heaven's sake——"

She cut in, icily, "You have a son."

"I'm not talking about children. I think you're being mighty unsatisfactory."

"Is that all you married me for?"

"That's a cattish, feminine way of putting a question. But if you want an answer to it, I'll answer it. The answer is yes."

"Not very exalted——"

"Oh, hush. Don't be silly. I wouldn't have married you if you'd been a boy, would I?"

She made an amused grimace.

"Well, go on, Vicky. Answer *that*."

"*You* are being silly."

"It answers your question. What do you expect me to do?"

She thrust herself away from him. An angry light flared for an instant in her eyes and then went out.

"I am your wife. That's your answer, Niles. I guess you can do whatever you please with me, and whenever you please. I fancy it's an old Grandolet custom."

Niles almost jumped to his feet. He looked at her steadily for a moment, and then, quite deliberately, he took her by the shoulders and shook her long and hard as if he meant to tear her apart. When he released her she swayed dizzily in the seat, but kept herself from falling. He stood for another moment, the anger in his face subsiding, leaving it still and contemptuous. He walked to the door with an air almost nonchalant.

Victoria was angry and humiliated and a little frightened.

[172]

For a few mild seconds she wished to scream, to throw things after him, smash the expanse of mirror before her—anything to lessen the fury that left her breathless and trembling. If he had struck her, or sworn at her, even. But to be shaken like a bad child! And that last expression on his face, that cold contempt which set her outside of his consideration. She kept tight hold on herself. If she did not retreat, if she did not make a single gesture of conciliation, she knew that she might be able to keep him away—maybe forever. She closed her eyes and thought hard for a moment. It was the first time she had questioned herself clearly on this phase of her feelings. Could there be anything wrong with *her?* Quickly she reassured herself on that point. She had heard, once or twice, fragments of talk. *Men were like that.*

And now the fear that she had felt vanished. She was the mother of young Julien Quintin, and that established her safety. Q-G. A faint emotion stirred her, something like tenderness, something like a jealous possession. Q-G. He was her son, a Grandolet, but her own son, and through him as it must always be, she thought, she came into the full realization of all that she wanted.

She drew back from this thought a little, shrinking from an implied crudeness that she did not mean. It had nothing to do with White Cloud itself as a place, a house, or anything material. No, nor position. It had somehow to do with dominion. Now she was free enough of the crisis just past to smile at the terms of her own thinking. Dominion. That was a fine, big word. Dominion over what? Goodness alone knew what some one of her unknown selves might be dreaming about, but it was a happily satisfying word, and the sound of it touched her wounded and threatened pride with healing and promise.

Niles sat for a long time that night in the echoing, shadowy rooms that were known as "Cousin Etienne's quarters." He was having a quick revulsion of feeling. Undoubtedly he was being tactless and inconsiderate. Victoria had come near to death. It might be more than months before she would, or could, return to her normal self. True, she had been a cool companion, but in a perverse sort of way he rather admired that. It was a behavior consonant with the concept of "ladies" that had somehow been bred into him. He knew, too, that such notions were old-fashioned, but the Grandolets were old-fashioned. He was pleased with the fact that they were. Grandfather Julien and Aunt Lucie and Flora's mother—all of them. Anachronisms, maybe. All right, then they would be anachronisms. Wasn't White Cloud itself a holdover from a past which, much as he might decry it in a practical sense, he loved with all of his heart? Yes, he was old-fashioned. He tried to conduct affairs in terms of today, but he would doubtless live and die in terms of a society and a code which had long since been lost and forgotten by the world.

He was deeply stricken as he remembered the childish scene he had had with Victoria—he had not actually felt the things he must have looked. He had chosen Victoria. He would stand by his choice. He would wait and see what changes would come, for he did not believe, not for a moment, that her shrinking and her open dislike of intimacies could be real or permanent.

He turned wearily to a long table littered with agricultural reports, papers, and books. He had told no one except Grandfather Julien of his new ventures, but his imagination was fired by plans he was making. He stopped for a moment, his pencil poised over the paper. It had been Victoria who had set him off on this trail. That day when she had asked who were the richest men in the region. He had had many a conference with Bob Alexander since then. Bob—God bless him!

Niles ran through the columns before him again. A sensation of fright dampened his face. Lord! White Cloud mortgaged out of sight—but he was not too much worried about that particular fact. No, it was the thought of a reckless gamble in oil lands that appeared just now to be completely mad. He shook his head, a smile rueful and reckless on his lips. He looked at this moment extraordinarily like Hippolyte d'Aupais.

TWELVE

NILES GRANDOLET PROSPERED. Within a few years the prospective oil lands began to be oil lands in fact. There was nothing spectacular, but one thing added to another, and by and by people began to speak of the rich Grandolets.

The countryside changed. There were good roads and electric lines, telephones, and a few automobiles. People knew more about each other.

"I hear Niles Grandolet is doing fine now."

"Sure, sure! Everything that boy touches turns into money."

"I heard his Yankee wife brought him his start, though."

"I don't know about that."

"Well, lots of those Northerners have got money—heaps of it."

"I don't know about Mrs. Grandolet. Very fine-looking woman. And I'm ready to bet she's the brains and git-up-and-git behind Niles."

"Wouldn't be surprised."

"Why, look, you know the Grandolets have always been mighty easygoing."

"That's so. Lazy, if you ask me."

" 'Course they were, all of 'em. Now, all at once, bang—branching out in every direction."

"They say she's smart as all get-out."

"She is. I've talked with her. But, Lord a'mighty, she's more uppity than any Grandolet ever was yet. Talks down to you— you know, like Bob Alexander's old man—'s if you wasn't good enough to come 'round to the front of the house."

"Like that, eh?"

"Yes, but smart all the same. Talks about crops and cattle and hogs like a man."

"Yankee way, I guess."

"Don't know. Never have seen many real Northerners."

"They're like that."

In other quarters, and in quite different circles, there was much talk, and similar talk. It was agreed that Victoria must furnish the brains and the initiative, and maybe the capital. Certainly, this wasn't like Niles or any other Grandolet. White Cloud fixed up like old times. Gardens beautiful beyond anything in a hundred miles. And, strangest of all, the gradual restoration of Far Félice, and the creation of a kind of botanical garden about it. It was going to be a show place someday.

Distances were breaking down now. Five or six years had made an amazing difference. Formerly, living in the country meant one was cut off most of the year from the nearest neighbors. Circles of acquaintance widened, and visiting was livelier.

The talk about the Grandolets was not all about their changing fortunes. Victoria was thoroughly considered, summed up, reconsidered, and talked about all over again. Generally she came out well with the men. A few women thought her interesting. Most of them were not comfortable in her presence, didn't know why, and so settled on a compromise between tolerance and dislike. A good many old acquaintances looked to Flora's mother for final opinions on Victoria, but Marie

Vélazy, for an inconsistent wonder, said little. Victoria was a Grandolet now, and there was no more to be said about it, and after a while most people forgot that Victoria hadn't always been there. She was a Grandolet, and when she talked of the house, told stories of its past and of dead Grandolets, she appeared to speak out of experience. What she said was so accepted.

So it was that all of the parts of the life at White Cloud moved somehow into a pattern. Forces of attraction and repulsion thrust the pieces into a sort of moving equilibrium. To all the world it appeared to be a settled group, accepting the play of individual eccentricities with the calm of an established belief in the basic security of the family. But there was not one of the Grandolets who felt or believed this. They were ranged—not exactly against each other, or against anything they could define—but in a sort of waiting design. There was a tension, more or less morbid, a certain watchfulness, a consciousness of double meaning and dissonant undertones in conversation, and an uneasy awareness of what was moving, out of sight, and behind one's back.

The one person least affected by all this was Grandfather Julien. He read his books, listened heavily, and now and then dropped quotations which left everyone wondering if he didn't see and sense more than anyone.

Aunt Lucie made her "good long visit" to Wyandotte. The fiction of the visit was maintained, although the stay had stretched from three to five and now to seven years.

Flora had no children and that was a subject no one mentioned, although Victoria rang diabolic changes on the notion that this whole region was *un endroit de la fécondité*.

Somewhere in these years a time arrived when Victoria

moved out of being either her real or fancied self, and became an actress. But she was not really aware of the curious part Orlou was playing. It was Orlou who shaded Victoria's feeling, established moods and attitudes. It was Orlou's talent for drama that appealed to Victoria's deep sense of play-acting. It was Orlou who set behind Victoria a real but unrecognized belief that White Cloud did reject what was not right for it.

Year by year White Cloud loomed even more clearly before her as a living personality, frighteningly alive with precisely those unknown factors she had talked of once—the leftover loves and hates, the desperations, the violences, all of which had been too great for the hearts and brains and lives of those who begot them and bore them here in the calm and exquisite denials of White Cloud itself.

She fancied herself moving among these invisible lightnings, safe because of her own pride and scorn, and so almost a ruler over them—a power able to use them and direct them. Where did her pride and scorn come from? A few times she wondered, wondered a bit fondly, as one might contemplate the possession and the sudden development of an unexpected talent. In any case, she knew that she and all that stirred in her heart were set over and apart from White Cloud, and set hard against it.

It was Far Félice that crystallized her emotional attitude. Her sense of possession began with it and extended to White Cloud quite as White Cloud seemed the child of that darker place crouching close to the levee.

Her complete projection of her dominion was visualized and realized in young Q-G. The boy, a slim and graceful figure, flitted about White Cloud with an eerie appearance of having been materialized out of the least earthly of elements. He was dark and quick. The deep brown Grandolet eyes had a very slight slant. This was apparently the only feature derived from Victoria. Q-G was quietly devoted to Niles, but he gave one the indefinable feeling of being without parents. His deference to Victoria was like the deference of a good-mannered child to a guest.

Victoria had heard of the rumors about her, that she had brought money to White Cloud, that she was the directing intelligence, the sagacious adviser, and all of the characteristic variations and exaggerations of the theme. She smiled with a deprecatory look in her eyes when any such mention was made, smiled and glanced away as if unwilling to take credit for what was done and forgotten. By and by her response to these ideas had the comforting quality of knowing just praise for good deeds. Unless she caught herself short she believed that even if she had not done exactly these things, she had certainly done others of equal value and importance.

It was easier and easier every day so to costume her mind for the part she played.

Niles lived on in Cousin Etienne's old rooms, but he was often at Wyandotte. He talked to Aunt Lucie and Flora about his plans. Only Flora's mother noticed how seldom Victoria's name entered the conversation, and how rarely any of them inquired about her.

Victoria's friends were mostly people new to White Cloud. They were an appreciative audience and the play moved on through phases of minor suspense to some sort of denouement which no one actually thought about, or even wondered about, but which everyone unconsciously felt and awaited.

"I don't know what it is about White Cloud, but I am always on edge a little when I'm there." Eva Pawling, whose husband, Chester Pawling, was a geologist, spoke rather eagerly, with a questioning lift to her sentence and a slight shine in her eye, as if she hoped someone would make an unfavorable report on the reason for her feeling.

"Victoria keeps your interest going. That's it, I'd say." Chester Pawling always seemed to mean something different from what he said. Eva looked at him doubtfully.

"I declare, I don't see how she puts up with Niles, though." Waite Gardner was a man of fifty-five and a loud champion of Victoria Grandolet.

"Why?" Eva could invest a single word with considerable dry comment.

"Well, my God a'mighty, he just sits there and stares at her. I'd say she hasn't got much in her life."

Chester flicked a quick glance at Waite Gardner. "She has us."

"Us?"

"Yes."

"What's that got to do with it?"

"Weren't you suggesting that she needs an audience?"

"No."

"Well, that's what Victoria loves, and that's what we are, and that's why she loves us—if and what and how so."

"I think Victoria Grandolet is a damn fine woman. Look at White Cloud *now*."

"I do—often."

"What are you getting at, Chester? You can't talk——"

"Oh, sit down, Waite. Don't be so picturesque. That's one thing about White Cloud 'now,' as you say. Everything is so damned picturesque you can't drink a julep around there without feeling symbolic and mysterious. You'd think the silver mugs came straight out of Circe's cupboard."

"You're just all on Niles' side."

Eva looked up quickly. "I didn't know there *were* sides."

"Well, well, I mean——"

Chester thumped his pipe against the sole of his shoe. "I know what you mean. You mean you think sides. Everybody talks sides. Therefore there *are* sides, because you and a lot of fool people are drawn up that way."

Waite Gardner blinked a bit stupidly. "Well, good Lord, don't fly down my throat. I just thought everybody kind of thought as I do."

"How is that?"

"That—that, well, that Victoria is away over Niles Grandolet's head, and——"

"I don't think that way. Niles Grandolet's a prince of a fellow."

"Oh, sure, sure. But I don't think he *gets* Victoria. Not at all, not at all."

Chester relighted his pipe. "I think he gets her, all right."

Victoria was enjoying herself. She was giving freedom and scope to her notions of what she wished to appear to be. She played at being grand, at being enigmatic, mysterious, capricious; she had moments of assuming a sort of high comedy; she was a fine lady hostess; she was the lonely stranger speaking hesitatingly as if she had to bring herself from a far habit of life. Through it all she managed with real skill to keep everyone at a distance. In achieving what looked like a spiritual remoteness she added the final footlight note of glamour to her performance. It was rather bewildering to most people; it was irritating to Niles and Flora; it was amazing to Aunt Lucie. To Victoria herself it was exhilarating. She reveled in a many-faceted seeming. In so doing she escaped ever being herself. She was still uncertain what herself might be, and there were times, many times, when she doubted that there was any longer anything left of the Victoria Dunstan who had become Victoria Grandolet.

"Victoria seems very happy." Aunt Lucie looked sharply at Marie Vélazy. "Even gay." She waited a moment. "I wonder if she really is? Poor child."

"Haven't you answered your own question?"

"How?"

"You said 'poor child.'"

"Yes, yes. So I did."

"I think Victoria enjoys herself."

"Oh, do you? Well, I do hope so. I don't wish anyone ill."

"I'm not saying she's happy."

"Oh, Marie, are you being clever again? You do confuse me so at times."

"I don't believe it."

"But you said——"

"I said she is enjoying herself. I don't think she enjoys any-one else. And happiness isn't a game of solitaire."

"Victoria is hardly solitary, Marie."

"She's playing some sort of solitaire with a cloud of wit-nesses."

"Cloud of witnesses? Isn't that from the Bible?"

"I don't know. But I do know Victoria has just that, and doesn't have a good time unless they are present. She's a prima donna."

Aunt Lucie rocked for a few moments. "That kind of leaves Niles out, doesn't it?"

Marie was repairing the beadwork on an old bag. She gave such a flounce that she spilled the box of beads. "Oh, dear! Touch that bell, please, Lucie."

An ascetic-faced maid, nearly white, came in. "Yes, ma'am?"

"Oh, Atlanta. I spilled those beads—all over the floor. Brush them up. Use a dustpan. Then—just throw them away. And, here."

"Yes, ma'am?"

"You can have the bag. I'm putting my eyes out. Take it all away."

After Atlanta had left the room, Marie said tensely, half under her breath, "Niles!"

"What do you mean, Marie? You make me so uneasy when you don't talk out."

"Why?"

"I'm afraid you know something I don't know."

"Well, I don't. You know just what all of us know. And it makes me so mad I see cross-eyed."

"Just which, or what does?"

"Oh, all that going-on up there at White Cloud. It's so theatrical I could spit."

"My dear!"

"I could. Poor Niles."

"I don't know how it is, but whatever we're talking about, sooner or later we get around to *her*."

"That's exactly what she wants, too."

"It seems, from all I can hear, to be like that all around. Everybody seems to be awfully interested——"

"Oh, yes. That's what she puts up. *So interesting*. Did you ever try to remember her talk after you leave there, try to analyze it, or even try to think *what* she talked about?"

"No."

"Well, you can't!"

"Can't what?"

"Can't remember it—what she talked about, or did. It's all a kind of legerdemain. She's fooling everybody."

"Well, Marie, we have to admit she's pretty good at it. Seems to me I can't remember any of us making such a success."

"Success! Lucie, you make me sick."

Aunt Lucie rocked again, rather placidly. Then her chair stopped, always a signal.

"Marie!"

"Now, what? Whenever you do that you're up to something."

"When I do what?"

"Rock and then stop."

"No, no. I was just going to ask——"

"Quick! I'm sure you've heard something."

"No. Just thinking. Have you ever noticed how much John stays up there, and how often he quotes her?"

Marie hissed her scorn. "John!"

"But he does."

"He always made fun of her ways. Come to think of it, he hasn't lately."

"Exactly. Last night he remarked on how much practical sense she has."

"He did, didn't he? The fool."

"Marie, do you think Victoria would try to bother little Flora that way?"

Marie laughed. "Lucie, you're a goose. Don't you know Flora *couldn't* be bothered that way?"

"Poor Flora."

"Yes. I should have put my foot down. But it was too late, anyway, I guess."

The two women exchanged glances. Aunt Lucie spoke quietly. "I didn't mean it could exactly *bother* Flora, not really,

[185]

but Victoria might enjoy placing Flora in a position where people could talk."

"Well, for heaven's sake, Lucie—well, sometimes I think you are as blind as can be."

"I don't understand you at all."

"Did you ever stop to think how much Niles is here with Flora?"

Aunt Lucie opened her eyes very wide. "Oh, my dear. Oh, Marie! Oh, dear, dear!"

"Can you blame them?"

"But, Marie, with their temperaments and——"

"Their heartaches——"

"It—well, couldn't it be dangerous?"

"How do I know? They're pretty nice people, basically, as good as our kind comes, which maybe isn't too good, but there's something about both of them——"

"I know. Something handed down—maybe good, maybe——"

Marie sniffed. "Probably too noble to break over—poor things."

"Oh, Marie——"

"Would you say no to such an idea?"

"Yes."

"Well, I guess I would, too." Marie laughed again. "Lucie, for all of your sharp brown eyes, I am sure as can be, you haven't noticed something I have."

"Now what?"

"Orlou!"

"What about Orlou?"

"Well, I've noticed it, and I've laughed inside. Orlou sees everything. Every time we're up there and Niles goes off somewhere with Flora, you know, moonlight nights, off in the gardens or someplace, Orlou follows them."

"Oh, Marie! How shocking that is!"

"You're misunderstanding Orlou altogether. She's not spying. Orlou is no more vulgar than you or I. No, she's guarding the family, that's all. Hovering—keeping them safe."

Aunt Lucie thought for a moment. She rolled her eyes with an unaccustomed drollery. "Or——"

"What?"

"Maybe she's being Brangäne!"

"Who? Oh! In that opera thing. I think you're mixed up a little, but—no, Orlou is on the side of the gods, I believe."

"I wonder if we know what side the gods are on."

John Connor had always thought he did not like Victoria, and he was sure she did not like him, but he had lately begun to realize that of all the Grandolet connections Victoria was the only one he could talk to. She no longer made him feel like a complete outsider incapable of understanding anything about this difficult family. Sometimes he was sure that she agreed with him but she never came out quite to say so.

Connor had done pretty well with Wyandotte, but he had not made it pay actually as well as Niles had. Niles was "in" with everyone. Niles was a Grandolet.

Long before the Connors had bought Rennover—and destroyed it—John had felt keenly enough what it was not to belong to the old order. He had set it down to the backward ways of this particular parish, remote and "out of things" as it was. He had been dazzled by his marriage to Flora Vélazy, but even in the first days of that marriage he was once more aware of elusive somethings that raised and kept an invisible barrier between him and Flora's relatives. Again he had tried to tell himself that they simply didn't understand the world at all, certainly not as it really was. They were "stuck up" about a past that was as dead as Rome. They'd come to some-day. After all, the Connors had started at the bottom and made themselves rich in one generation. Something none of the Grandolets or Vélazys had ever done. No, and by God, they *couldn't*. They didn't have the abilities. They could do well enough when they had so much to go on, and with everyone in the state who knew the Grandolets ready to help them, giving them the preference, clearing an inside track for them on every chance.

For a long time John Connor rested comfortably on those beliefs. And then he awoke to a new unease. He didn't know how it came about. Sometimes he tried to trace his new feelings. He couldn't remember exactly when he began to wonder if maybe all of these people had something he didn't have, that maybe the way they talked their own language and went on and on so consistently in their curious ways might not have something to it. Maybe it was just a special way of playing life, like a game, that made it come out in certain predictable results. He was damned if he understood half the time what they were saying, and he was equally damned if he knew what they thought about anything.

He'd been tremendously taken with Flora. He had known all kinds of girls, but he hadn't really gotten very near to any of that old crowd. She was pretty—Lord, yes, and her soft little ways, and her movements—well, she set him on fire from the beginning. He never got over being surprised at how easy she had been to win. He guessed that away from Louisiana, where he had as good a chance as anyone, he had showed up all right. She had seen him as he really was. Yes, that must have been it.

Afterward? Well, afterward, a lot of the old tormenting questions began to come up. She had married him, and he had moved to Wyandotte and had met the innumerable cousins, but he always felt like a visitor. He meant to be the master of the house. He tried the simple matter of being naturally the host. Even that he never quite managed. It was exactly as if something had slipped each time. It was either Flora or her mother who suddenly stood where he should have been. Why, damn it, even Niles looked and acted more as if he were the man of the place.

Many small realizations came to him gradually. Naturally, the family had been polite about speaking French. He understood some of the lingo, of course, but that was mostly Cajun French. He couldn't understand this kind of French at all. Often they forgot and were talking a mile a minute before they remembered. It gave him an uncomfortable feeling that what they said in English was not even on the same subject. He kept thinking he'd learn to speak French, but he didn't really approve of the idea. This was the United States, wasn't it? Another generation and all of these old-time hangovers would be gone.

He was never quite certain just when he came to the conclusion that he would always be something of an outsider. The feeling had arrived by imperceptible degrees. He had thought maybe everything would be different if Flora had some kids, but that hope had died. He wondered what was the matter with her. That, now—that was another thing. He could not understand why he actually had not been able to talk to her about it. She was his wife, and all that, but somehow that intimate discussion never arrived.

It must have been about that time, when his opinion of himself and his confidence were at a low ebb, that he had found himself talking pretty freely to Victoria. He couldn't recall that she had ever asked him a question. No, he was sure she hadn't. For a long time he had been afraid of her. She had a damned clever way of making fun of people when they didn't know it or realize it. He thought she had never done that to him, but once or twice he had suspected her.

When she had that botanist fellow over from the university to make suggestions about the gardens at Far Félice—then it was, he supposed, he began to be friendlier with her. He had been able to locate a lot of plants and stuff they wanted up there. That was an interesting idea Victoria had had about Far Félice. It wouldn't be surprising if that should become a famous restoration. You could charge admission to a place like that and make your money back.

Anyway, he felt a bit easier with Victoria than he did with anyone else.

It was at Far Félice one day, when they were sitting out in the big half circle of crape myrtles, that he had let himself go for the first time.

"It's the doggonedest country around here. I don't think I ever would feel natural in it."

"Why?" Victoria had smiled as she glanced at him. Looked as if she already knew the answer better than he did. A way she had.

"I don't know. It's big country. Great big plantations and all that, but I don't feel free in it. I can't let out, seems like. The way I can in Texas."

"What is it, do you think?" Again she had smiled that provoking, dreamy little smile.

"I feel hemmed in, that's all I know about it."

"Yes." She had sounded as if she were answering herself, not him.

"Do you feel that way?"

"I was born in a very different kind of country, you know." It had seemed an answer, and yet it wasn't.

"Why, my God, Victoria, I haven't ever said this before, but I feel like I'm getting smaller and smaller all the time."

"What do you wish to do?" She turned eagerly, like an adult starting a game with a child. "Tell me, John, what would you rather do than anything in the world?"

He looked startled. He hadn't thought really of doing anything different. He only wished to be happier doing what he was doing now. But he felt that Victoria expected an interesting answer from him, and he rallied his imagination.

"I—I guess I'd like to sell things, maybe—on a big scale, you know, or—or make something. I don't know. I'm not doing anything as it is."

"Aren't you being a successful planter?"

"On Flora's lands."

"What about Rennover?"

"Leased to my cousin."

"For how long?"

"On an annual basis."

Victoria looked regretful, he thought, as if he were losing something and didn't realize it as well as she did. He had a sudden burst of feeling about Rennover.

"Do you know, Victoria, I—I get homesick for Rennover, even if I wasn't there more'n about five years. I feel shut up at Wyandotte."

"Is Rennover nice?"

"After we built a new place. It's open. You're so damned smothered in these places with trees and shrubbery and vines."

"It isn't the vines and the shrubbery, John."

"Well, what is it then?"

"It's other things—things that have been growing for a long time, in the same way. Customs, little ways——"

"That's it, Vic! My God, but you hit the nail on the head

then! I feel like the inside of my head is full of winding, twining, twisting stuff—do you know what dodder is?"

"Dodder?"

"Sure. It's a parasite plant. Looks like a mess of yellow thread. Grows like crazy, snarls and tangles and smothers things."

"I see. I understand."

John laughed shortly. "Do you know what people call it? It'll make you laugh."

"What?"

"*Love vine*. Yes, sir, love vine. My God!"

Victoria did not laugh. She looked at him steadily for a moment. It made him think that he had touched the rim of some secret tragic subject. He felt suddenly as if they were drawn closer together than they had ever been before.

That talk with Victoria had been only a beginning. This kind of intimacy, he realized, did not remain at a point. It progressed by sudden and disturbing steps. He told her a great deal about himself. Some of it was true, some of it wasn't. He tried always to make it as interesting as possible. He felt that when Victoria was interested, he had to be interesting.

What amazed John Connor more than a little was just how interesting he *did* seem to be. It was quite remarkable how well Victoria understood him. There were odd and difficult aspects of her, too, which puzzled him. She didn't tell him anything about herself, not really. She hinted, and maybe that was as much as a woman of her kind could do. Damned loyal of her, and fine. More loyal than the Grandolets, or Niles, deserved. Kept a stiff upper lip. It flattered him, too, that she assumed he understood more about her than he did.

Everything in their friendship seemed to happen before he knew it. He had let confidences go and wondered afterward how he had gotten started on this or that subject. It was the same about Flora. Certainly, Victoria never did say anything about Flora. No, she had really praised Flora, and tried to explain the Vélazys to him. But it hadn't improved his patience with Flora, or his temper.

There was the ever-recurring question of Wyandotte and Rennover. He knew that Victoria had never breathed a suggestion that he should cut himself loose from the Vélazys and the Grandolets and take Flora to live at Rennover. She hadn't *said* it, but she had, well, she had sort of *illustrated* the idea with parables and the like. She seemed to think or feel, at least he guessed she did, that, if he took his wife to live at his own place in his own way, she would fit into his world after a while. Victoria did as good as say that his world was real and new and full of possibilities, while this walled-in existence here on the river was just a dreamlike thing. These people clung to as many of the old ways of living and thinking as they could. But that was just a drug to keep the dream going, to keep them from realizing that they didn't even belong to the present. They would see in a hurry how unimportant they were, once they were removed from a setting which perpetuated an illusion. Victoria didn't make application of these ideas directly to Flora. But he knew what she meant. Victoria was a lady, and she was married into the Grandolet family, and there were, of course, some things she couldn't say. But he understood. He was not stupid.

He thought about it for a long time. The notion of simply picking up and going to Rennover with Flora whether she liked it or not occupied his fancy for many months. He turned the plan over and over in his mind, this way and that. But even as he did this, he realized how intricately Flora's life was interwoven with all of the lives of her family—present and past. Yes, that was the worst of it. *The past.* Maybe he could cut her clear of the present, even of her razor-tongued mother, but the past—that was something else. It was all like that confounded love vine he had told Victoria about.

And then, effortlessly, he thought about Rennover without Flora. It came about as simply as that. At first he thought he'd just go over for a while, give himself a recess. The shadowy suggestion in his mind became an idea, the idea became a plan. But he said nothing to Victoria about the new avenue his wishes were now traveling. He was sure that all that was good and noble in Victoria would rise to dissuade him. You couldn't argue with her. She was too clever, and she was always looking over your head and far away as if she saw circumstances and consequences hidden from you. Whatever circumstances and consequences there might be, he would face alone and deal with in his own way. He was a practical man. It was possible that even Victoria was a bit drugged with dreams herself. She probably couldn't fully understand a completely practical world and a downright sensible way of conducting matters.

Niles had ridden over to Wyandotte to see Flora. It was late fall, and perfect weather lay over the land like a gentle enchantment.

"Come out, Flora, let's walk in the garden. I have to talk to you."

"Has anything happened, Niles?"

"Nothing new."

That was as near as Niles ever approached the subject of any possible unhappiness or discord at White Cloud. By tacit agreement he and Flora spoke little of Victoria. The continued stay of Aunt Lucie at Wyandotte was never discussed.

"How is your grandfather? He seemed much changed when I saw him."

"He changes less than you think. But he does seem rather withdrawn from—from everything, doesn't he?"

"Yes, I suppose so. Victoria pays a good deal of attention to him and he likes that. And Q-G?"

"Wonderful. He likes his tutor, but I think he learns more from Grandfather Julien. He practically lives in the old gentleman's pocket."

"It's a grand influence, Niles, for him."

They walked on a few moments. The walks had a thin tapestry of leaves, the shrubbery had taken on a used and tired look, but there were late flowers and the air was still and warm. Niles glanced sideways at Flora. Poor little Flora. He wondered about her and the state of her mind and heart, but that, too, was a world shut off from everyday talk. She was lovelier, he thought, than she had ever been. No longer childish, but bearing a manner of youthful courage and freshness.

"Niles!" She had stopped suddenly and her eyes caught his look of question. "What were you about to ask?"

"Nothing."

"Honest?"

"Yes."

"You're a poor liar, Niles, my old darling. But I was going to ask an impertinent question. May I? And will you not answer if you don't want to?"

"Ask away."

"How much really has Victoria to do with Q-G's training?"

Niles looked away. He answered quietly and distantly, as if they were speaking of some subject of no interest to either of them.

"Very little, really. She takes him about some—to Far Félice, which he loves—talks to him in—in her way."

"I suppose I understand. I don't know if I do or not. I just wish to be reassured, if you'll let me say that this once."

"Q-G is making himself, as far as I can see, after a legend. He's obsessed with White Cloud and Grandfather's stories. He's building something on that."

"I see. That answers my question."

Niles ignored her comment. He went on talking to himself apparently. "Q-G is a strange child, but he is all Grandolet—old, old Grandolet. He's as archaic as—as chivalry, or something like that. I don't know where it all comes from. But he's growing up into something that—I don't know how to say it, as—as if he'd been made out of the air of White Cloud rather than born of flesh and blood."

"He looks it, too."

"Oh, I guess we were all dreamers. It isn't just that. But if there have been fine strains anywhere, I—I think they were saved up for him. And yet, I'm afraid for him."

"Why?"

"The otherworldliness of him, coupled with the blazing temper all of us have. I can't keep him from the real world, and he isn't living in a real world now——"

"Oh, Niles, I wouldn't worry about that. I have an idea every parent in the world has thought and felt that way. The world is always new, and I guess it is always dangerous. Every one has to meet his own dangers. You have only to reassure yourself about qualities."

"Where did you learn all of that? So wise!"

"And me so young!" She laughed, but Niles was suddenly grave.

"Yes," he said.

"What are you here for today, Niles? There's something on your mind."

"Yes. Business."

"Oh!"

"I haven't been so lucky the past eighteen months, Flora."

"I'm sorry, Niles. What is it?"

"I've about used up the timber at Far Félice. The wells are not so good. I should have paid off the mortgage on White Cloud when I had money. I can't now."

"Does that make any difference? Silly."

"But I need a lot more money."

"If I have enough——"

"That's what I came for, you blessed angel. I need thirty thousand dollars. Far Félice security, and it isn't worth a fraction of it. The house isn't included in that security, of course. That belongs to Victoria."

"Niles, you know I don't want mortgages and all that sort of thing."

"But that's the way I'd want it."

"Whatever you say."

"But I must tell you that I'm going to gamble like the devil. Long chances. I'll make a lot, or——"

"Can you go down to New Orleans to arrange there?"

"Yes."

"My affairs remain my own, and separate."

"I want you to tell your mother first of all."

"But not John."

He looked long and hard at her, then away, then back again.

"As you wish."

"Now, that's out of the way. Let's go to Aunt Lucie. She's always so crazily glad to see you."

THIRTEEN

"A LIMBO OF INDECISION." Niles said the words over to himself. He could not remember where he had heard the phrase. Maybe he had read it. Trite enough, in any case. But the reality was painful, if anyone could call it a reality. Indecision, chronic indecision, was a hovering between two realities, as neutral and as gray as Dante's contemptible vestibule to hell.

Contradictory feelings and impulses besieged his misty retreat. Like every other human being trained in the ways of formalized existence, he sometimes found it difficult to know which emotions were real and which ones were word-made counterfeits—simulants made to stand as deceits for convention. Niles was old-fashioned.

He repeated to himself words and sentences descriptive of his attitude and relation to Victoria. But these incantations were impotent. An emotion once expressed in the powerful institutions of society could stand rigid and strong, preserving the form of life long after life had ceased to exist. Like a dead tree.

His marriage, and his carefully preserved appearance of family. *Simulacrum.* He made a sardonic grimace. A fine word—a fine old word. Too fine a word altogether for the thing it described. A sham. A shoddy imitation. Latin words were always like that. He wondered for a moment if the preference for Latin magnificence wasn't just a poor human device for erecting imposing and endurable seeming. He brought himself up short. Yes, and wasn't such elementary speculation as this trifling with a word one of his own retreats from direct encounter with his grim problems?

Victoria was the reality. His marriage. But his house was a figment of hypocritical pretense.

Whatever his feeling for Victoria had been—and it might well have grown into something warm and lasting, something comforting and supporting—whether passion or caprice, had atrophied. He could have ignored her long ago, he could have consoled himself one way or another, he could have retreated emotionally into a premature asceticism—possibly, or he could have entered into an agreeable and dignified friendship, if Victoria had not seemed so purposely intent on poisoning the atmosphere of peace at White Cloud. What was she about? That her behavior was a performance he had known for a long time. But who was her invisible audience, anyway? From where could she draw the applause that her soul must somehow demand? What incredible faculty of mind or freakish attribute of character was satisfied by the unnatural routine she imposed upon herself?

He thought, but he could not be quite clear about his finding, that in some way he could not even wish to understand, Victoria must herself be both the watcher and the watched.

Over and over again, he told himself that he no longer cared what she did, what she thought, or if she might be happy or unhappy, and day by day he guarded the secret scene of White Cloud's wordless drama.

Over and over again, he told himself that his feeling for Flora was only a deepening of his old affection, deepened with pity because he guessed the devastation that lay back of her touching little pretenses. He was not fooled by Flora.

Victoria? No, he could never face in that direction again. But she was the mother of Q-G.

The world outside of the walls of White Cloud was big enough for him to lose himself, demanding enough to make him work, interesting enough, he thought, to make him forget. But he knew also that he lived not in a limbo of indecision, but in a bright, particular hell of denial, and that he saw no way out of it.

Outwardly, life at White Cloud flowed serenely.

The mysterious counterpoint of human lives moved and wove its invisible patterns. No one seemed aware of the tightening design, of the stresses and withheld resolutions.

Everyone said Victoria Grandolet was a brilliant hostess. It was a happiness, they repeated, that White Cloud showed once more a revival of the old spacious life—almost like the old days. And wasn't Niles a lucky person?

Occasionally there were small half-spoken comments—not quite gossip, not quite accusation, but insinuating questions, maybe, about Niles and Flora.

Victoria had often been annoyed by that one little spot of unease in her mind. Niles and Flora: Flora and Niles. She could not admit conscience. One took what was necessary in this world, and the one strong enough to take was properly the one to whom things belonged. But a feeling persisted—a faint sense of threat. It was like the appearance of heat lightning against a seemingly calm horizon, and it carried an exasperating quality of threat with it. Victoria could face some very frank self-examination. She could ask herself if she felt any remorse in remembering how ruthlessly she had taken Niles from Flora, and she could truthfully answer herself that she felt nothing. She could ask herself if there was any possible justification for holding Niles at a distance, and she could make satisfactory reply by the mere protest of her shrinking flesh. She could answer all these tiny, persistent questions, and she could still know that a residue of unrest remained, and a thin presence of ghostly fear.

When bits of near gossip about Flora and Niles flitted past her ears she was not surprised. How complete a justification of herself lay there in those floating fragments of suggestion! It was difficult to remember sometimes that she had started it herself. She had been able to raise quick suspicions by the lift of an eyebrow, by a restrained smile, or by a mere silence. If whispered stories could grow so easily there must be a favorable soil of fact.

Victoria could feel triumphant and still miss the restful complement of happiness. She had no clear definition of happiness in her mind and, in truth, she seldom thought about happiness. Having set up so many counterfeits, she had come to believe them real.

She wondered sometimes if she could be capable of jealousy. How would she feel if it could be brought to her that the stories about Niles and Flora were true?

Victoria comforted herself, and reassured herself in a strange way. She fell back on a secure knowledge that Niles was an honorable man.

One morning a note was handed to Niles at the breakfast table. He glanced at it. "From Flora. That's funny. Excuse me, please."

Niles read the few lines, folded the note, and laid it on the table. Grandfather Julien waited a moment. "Nothing wrong at Wyandotte, I hope?"

Niles shrugged. "I don't know. Flora wants to see me right away. Business, I guess, of some kind."

He finished breakfast quickly and arose.

"May I come with you?" Q-G was already on his feet.

"What about your lessons?"

Q-G grinned guiltily. "All right, all right." But it was evident that he did not expect his ready agreement to be taken seriously. He kept an eager, expectant face turned toward Niles.

It was hard for Niles to refuse anything to Q-G. The boy seemed fairly to quiver. He looked as if a denial would be crushing.

"Stop that, Q-G!" Niles laughed, his laughter tempered with a kind of exasperation.

"Stop what?" Q-G put on a bewildered expression.

"You know well enough what I mean."

"*I* don't know what you mean, Niles." Grandfather Julien managed one of his serious-looking smiles and was instantly rewarded with a flash of gratitude from Q-G.

Niles looked at Julien with mock resignation. "Both of you know what I mean. Q-G invents this tremendous eagerness, as if each request were a matter of tremendous importance."

"Riding out with you is tremendously important." Q-G said this slyly.

"Why, Q-G! Down to your last resort, eh?"

"I don't know what you mean."

"Flattery, that's what."

"*Comment?*"

"*Enjolement.*"

"*Je ne m'abaisserais pas, comme ça.*"

Niles and Grandfather Julien shouted with laughter, but Q-G kept his extravagant dignity.

"Ask your mother what she thinks about running away from your lessons."

Q-G turned halfway toward her, but he did not ask.

Victoria leaned back in her chair. "I was just wondering how long it would take the two of you to arrive at the inevitable."

"Oh, Mother, you use such difficult words!"

"I mean, darling, that I'm surprised at you."

"Why?"

"Not knowing from the first that of course your father would take you to Wyandotte."

"Oh—I can go? It's a permission?"

"I was just recognizing the situation, Q-G."

Niles pushed his chair away from the table. "Don't tease the child, Victoria."

Q-G looked uncomfortable. He said very quietly, "May I go, Father?"

"Certainly."

Q-G circled the table with a sudden stamping dance.

Grandfather Julien held his hands to his head. "What kind of performance is that?"

"*C'est la bamboula!*"

Q-G tore out of the room before any amendments could be made to the happy conclusion. Niles arose.

Victoria went upstairs, and a few minutes later Orlou brought the mail.

"Luther's just come up from the box."

Victoria glanced through the half-dozen letters. She started a little. There was one from John Connor, and it was postmarked New Orleans. She hadn't known John was away.

The note was hurriedly scrawled on a half sheet of hotel note paper.

Dear Vic:

You know by this time I guess that I've made up my mind. It's going to be Rennover, and never Wyandotte again, as long as I live. But first, I've got to make this little trip to Mexico. I guess you'll hear about that, too.

If it hadn't been for you, I don't believe I could have done this. Thanks for the backing.

JOHN C.

So! That was why Flora had sent for Niles this morning. John and Flora would not be at Wyandotte any more. She felt a keen exultation rise in her breast. But she would have to be careful now about one thing. Maybe Aunt Lucie would wish to return to White Cloud. Though she might wish to stay at Wyandotte with Marie Vélazy—or even at New Orleans.

That was an indiscreet sentence of John's: "If it hadn't been for you . . ." She picked up the letter from the table, tore it across, and burned it in the fireplace. She hoped he had more sense than to say that to Flora.

Her step was light as she went downstairs.

Shortly before lunch Niles returned. She heard him coming toward her sitting room. She set her face carefully.

"Oh, back already, Niles?"

"Yes." He dropped rather wearily into a chair. Victoria watched him. He looked terribly upset. For an instant she felt a disturbing beat in her brain. Was it going to mean that much to Niles?

"I have some rather astonishing news from Wyandotte, Victoria."

"Yes? What has happened?"

"John has gone away."

She looked at him blankly. It was a curious way to put it,

she thought. Then she realized that Niles wasn't saying what she expected.

"Gone away? Why?"

"I don't know. Just—gone."

"Is he going to Rennover, is that it?" The question came of itself.

"No, no. You don't understand. He's gone. He has left Flora."

Victoria sank back in her chair. "Niles! I don't believe it."

"It's true enough. She had a long letter from him this morning. He didn't say a word to her before he left. Too much of a coward, I guess."

"Where is he going?"

"Right now to Central America—for a divorce."

Victoria flushed darkly. She brought her hand down hard on the arm of her chair. *"The fool! The fool!"*

Niles looked at her in surprise. He nodded. "Yes, he is. An even sillier fool than I could have guessed."

"I thought——"

"What did you think?" Niles almost jumped at her.

"I thought he was unhappy at Wyandotte."

"Oh, God! That clodhopper. *Unhappy!*"

"What does Flora say?"

"What would you expect her to say?"

"I don't really know, Niles. I don't know how Flora feels about—anything."

"Don't you?"

"Of course not."

"She doesn't say anything."

"It's humiliating for her, isn't it?"

"Humiliating? I don't think that's the right word. I think she's damn lucky to be rid of him."

"Oh."

"Vick, did you know anything about this?"

"What are you talking about? Certainly not." There was such a tone of truth in her voice that Niles believed her. "I shouldn't have been surprised if he had insisted on going back to Rennover with Flora, but I should not have guessed this."

"Well, anyhow, it's over with, done with, finished, thank God!"

"What do you suppose she will do? Go back to New Orleans?"

"No."

"She won't want to stay at Wyandotte, will she?"

"Why not? She's not alone."

"And the plantation?"

"I'm going to take over, just as before."

"I see."

Victoria said the words in a quiet tone that managed to sound eloquent with unspoken comment. It was a trick of hers, Niles thought, and a maddening one. He had seen her use it often when he knew that she could think of nothing to say. She could achieve a whole constellation of inference, implication, and insinuation by a simple hesitation. It was the kind of thing one could not answer without being put in the wrong by the very act of answering. Niles had discovered, however, that the one possible reply was not to reply at all.

He sat quite still, fingering a cigarette, looking at her, and watching the slow recoil of her concealed innuendo. Presently he muttered a word or two and left the room.

Victoria sat looking at the yellowed papers before her. She had a momentary impulse to dash all of them into the fireplace. She could not just now return to family research. This new situation was wholly unexpected. It was too much like a chess move from an opponent which exposed a dozen weaknesses and left all of one's strategy useless. She could not say clearly to herself that she had been engaged in a strategy of any kind. She had believed of late in a kind of personal destiny, and that others would act as she had expected and anticipated because of the character she had assumed them to possess. She questioned herself abruptly on this.

Victoria was not without a highly realistic but limited endowment of common sense. At least expected moments this faculty intruded itself. She would bring herself up violently and scatter her fanciful thinking, her colorful imaginings, and her dramatizations of the commonplace. At such times she saw the Grandolets as they obviously saw themselves, and as they described themselves—"simple country people engaged in making a living." For fleeting moments she heard their utterances without overtones, she saw their actions as direct means to open ends, she saw White Cloud as a fine old relic of another way of life, and even herself as merely an outsider who had fortunately married into a family whose ways were unfamiliar. But always the mood left her with a renewed sense that this was by no means all. And her own self stood farther than ever to one side, heightening the exotic quality of her living and her thinking by a kind of inner distance, insisting on strangeness, and importance, and whispering anew of the things that lurked beyond obvious appearance.

She reimagined the mystic powers of White Cloud over those who passed its doorway. She redramatized a conflict between the house and herself in which she was the worthy conqueror of its curious being. She felt the dark potency of Far Félice, her own ally and her own weapon, but she did not and could not persuade these fancies into the controlling bonds of words. She dealt more and more with moods and intuitions, she looked more and more upon shadows cast by shadows, and established herself in a dwelling actually more familiar than the concrete one she could reach out and touch with her fingers.

There was a constant happening, however, that stalked this lonely road of her imagining. When one comes to believe in shadows, and begins to create a world to hold them, those very shadows take on dimensions. They turn and reveal other than expected faces. Victoria knew this. She knew it was happening to her. She could disavow its reality, but she could not turn her eyes away from it, nor refuse the suggestions of its self-active life.

She had been reading lately. New books with new theories of the mind. She read and rejected the resemblance of some of her moods and feelings to the first faint rise of hysteria. The definitions and descriptions did not spread a light of cooler reason over the objects and features of her mind's dark hinterland. Rather did these pages of probing science verify for her the hard and real existence of what she could otherwise have believed transparent evocations of her fancy.

She looked squarely into the grinning face of hysteria and disavowed it. She was not to be thus deceived.

She turned from abstraction and generalities to the particular. White Cloud did actually exert an especial and predictable spell. The expression of the qualities that gave it an actual existence clung to it like the very shadow of itself. Here, channeled through the long decades and centuries, were the essences of the ancient Grandolets, rising again and again from the dead, to live out their incompleteness in the days of the living. It was true. She believed it.

White Cloud, she believed, had tried to reject her. Not, maybe, because she was "not proper to it," but because it knew her strength. It had ended by fearing her, and she had come to feel its subservience. That was in the time she had come fully to understand Isabella Niles, and when she understood her she no longer envied her. She, Victoria Dunstan, had long ago become Victoria Grandolet and a deeper Grandolet than Isabella.

Victoria had to tell Grandfather Julien about John Connor. The old man listened without moving. But his eyes flashed.

"Gone, eh?"

"Yes."

"White trash. Thank God there were no children."

Victoria did not answer.

"We've some disparate strains in our blood, Victoria, wild strains, quixotic, devilish, maybe, but we're still somebody. Whatever has come in has been passed down by time, shaped by consistent pressures. Mix in something like John Connor and you breed nobodies. Why don't you ask Flora and her mother to come here? What's the sense of their living alone down there at Wyandotte?"

Victoria shook her head. "Flora will be happier there, Grandfather. That's her world, too."

He looked quickly at her. "You travel alone, don't you, Victoria?"

She was startled but she did not show it. She answered simply, "Yes."

"Maybe you know best. All of us do the same, I guess. We are so infernally alone, aren't we? Walled in, deaf and blind. So, Connor is gone. Poor Flora."

"But you said——"

"I was thinking of the family then. I'm thinking about Flora now. I love Flora. She's been heated."

Victoria held her breath. What was he going to say next? But Grandfather Julien was not thinking of Victoria, nor of Flora.

"Cheated," he repeated. "But everyone is, one way or another.

"But," he went on, "it seems to matter little enough in the end what happens to the individual."

"You are not going to say that things always work out all right—finally, I mean?"

"Heavens, no, Victoria. I'm not such a simpleton. I was thinking of families. Individuals behave terribly; they are wrongheaded, wronghearted; they betray themselves, and others; but sometimes the principal thread remains unbroken—through all the generations."

"Grandfather Julien, you are often a bit mystical about family. It seems so to me, at least, and I don't always understand you."

Julien closed the book he was holding, took off his glasses, and squinted narrowly at Victoria. "I suppose I am more than just a bit mystical, my child. It may be that it is the Catholic temperament. It isn't surprising, either, that you don't always understand. Living in a world of—well, a kind of make-believe, as I think you sometimes do, isn't being mystical."

"Do you think I do that?"

"What?"

"Live in a world of make-believe."

"Part of you does, yes."

She laid her hand over his. "Tell me about it. I think I don't agree with you."

"You don't understand the Grandolets."

She drew her hand away. She was astonished and genuinely hurt. "Why, Grandfather Julien! You've said yourself——"

"Oh, I know, I know. You understand us separately, and perhaps, simply, as human beings."

"Is there anything else?"

"My dear! It's the rest that's important."

She looked annoyed. "You bewilder me."

"Well, take me, for instance. I'm one kind of person as Julien Grandolet. My own temperament, wishes, habits, likes, and so forth. As a link in a family chain, I'm something else— something more, I should say."

"You're right about one thing. I simply don't know what you are talking about!"

"*Voilà!*"

"But, after all, you're just talking about a special behavior, a family tradition. That's certainly not difficult to see or to understand."

"It's not what I am talking about. Look, Victoria, that branch of coral there on my table."

"Yes."

"And, by the way, how disappointing Buffon is on coral! Just a note. Fancy missing such an opportunity!"

Victoria turned her head with a sort of mock admonishment. "The patient coral, building his little bit, deep under the sea. I have heard my father dwell on it in sermons!"

"You miss the point. A family, such as ours, or any family of basic purpose, builds better than it knows. The individuals are like the individual atoms of life that died to make that fantasy there under that glass bell. Not one of them could have guessed the ultimate shape of beauty he was helping to create. We are like them. Each one of us dies and sheds his flesh and with that flesh all that he was as an individual. His failures, his passions, his sins. But something remains, a tiny, tiny residue——"

"Aren't you talking simple evolution?"

"My dear Victoria! As I said, you do not comprehend what it is that is a family."

"Very well, what is it, then? I'm willing to learn."

Julien smiled, a fleeting smile that went over his face like a small wave of many varied expressions. "I don't ask that you be respectful of me. Who am I? But you do not really know how to be respectful of ideas that are more important than either one of us."

"I'm sorry."

"*Entendons-nous!* I am not able to say what it is that we leave as our small contribution. If anyone could say precisely, we should all be wiser than we are, is it not so? But, I think, it may be that *I feel,* and that is why you call me mystical. I think it may be an accent on beauty."

Julien peered at her with a half-shy, half-cynical expression. He wagged his head sagely. "It is for the angels to laugh that I essay such an explanation, me. I am not a philosopher. Nevertheless, it may be that it is just that. Beauty—real or abstract, it does not matter. They are but two aspects of the same thing."

"Pagan——"

He cut her short. "Victoria, maybe you are good, maybe no: I do not even guess. It is possible that you could be wicked, *but* you can think only as a puritan. Pagan? Assuredly. And so I think if there is in the hidden purpose of a family an unknown intention toward——" He pointed at the coral branch. "Let us say, something like that, then we become superior. It distinguishes us from that which goes nowhere, that which is without its secret purpose."

"You will say now that it is from God, and that, Grandfather Julien, is the ultimate egotism of——"

[212]

"Of such as we?"

"I wasn't going to say that."

"But I will accept that, and agree. Yes: such as we."

"You are proud, aren't you, and stiff-necked?"

"I hope so, my dear. I admire greatly the neck which knows nothing of humility. Humility! That is for those who are trash. Ah, and you spoke of God! Do I say this—this abstraction we discuss comes from God? I have not said so, but I should not fear to say so."

Victoria patted his hand again.

"Do you secretly mock at my ideas, Victoria?"

"Je ne pense à rien moins qu'à cela!"

"The family," he said musingly. "It is greater than the law—or the church. Because it is a shape of life: it has one current of blood, generation after generation. Its unknown purposes and intentions drive upon that flood. We say 'of our blood': it is our most significant, our most profound utterance. The decisions of the blood are the directions of eternity."

Victoria did not speak. She watched him. His eyes looked as though all of the violent tempers of life had been drained from them, leaving their vision clear and wise and deeply mournful.

FOURTEEN

Niles went often to Wyandotte that winter. He had settled easily into an undefined place in the household. Certainly Wyandotte felt much more like home than did White Cloud. Here he was at ease. The talk was casual, familiar, and understandable. Sometimes he was near to breaking under Victoria's cryptic, tense, dramatic conversation. She seemed increasingly unable to make the simplest statement, the most obvious kind of answer to a question, without loading it with double meaning.

Flora was curled up this February day in the corner of a big couch. She stared at the fire. Neither had spoken for some time.

"It was my own mistake," she said suddenly.

Niles looked up, a bit startled. They had not spoken of John, but he knew she was thinking of him.

"I should have married a man of my own kind. If at all."

"There aren't any of your kind, Flora."

"I'm serious, Niles."

"Well, it's——"

"I know what you're going to say. 'It's all over and done with.' I heard that a thousand times this winter. Such a thing is probably never over and done with."

Niles straightened in his chair. "Flora, you aren't still in love with John Connor?"

"I never was, Niles. Now don't ask me why I married him."

"I wasn't going to. I might as well ask why I married Victoria."

Flora spoke slowly after a long moment. "You married Victoria because you idealized her, I think. It was understandable, Niles."

"Listen, Flora. I've never spoken of this before, and maybe I never will again. But I—I think I married someone who never existed—never could exist."

"What has she wanted, I wonder?"

"I don't know. Maybe I should feel sorry for Victoria. I suppose she married someone who didn't exist, either."

"You are kinder than I can be."

"What *has* she wanted, Flora? What, that she couldn't have found?"

"I have a sort of intuition about her. I may be all wrong, but it's something like this. White Cloud, Niles, isn't an easy place for a stranger to move into. Victoria began some sort of make-believe, right at the beginning. She was bolstering herself, somehow—*why,* I don't know. But she fell into that way, and couldn't stop."

"I simply don't know what you are talking about."

"I imagine not. I'm just thinking. She got in deeper and deeper—oh, Niles, can't you see she's playing a role? She always did that somewhat. She's gotten some sort of comfort out of it, or else it's something she's felt she could use against White Cloud——"

"Why, in heaven's name, does she have to use anything against White Cloud? It's her own home."

"But you do feel that she does, don't you?"

"Well, maybe. I don't know. I still don't see *why*."

"She's been up against White Cloud somehow. The place itself injured her some way——"

"Injured?"

"All inside, I mean. Mentally, or something. She has always talked strangely about it."

"I know. 'White Cloud rejects.'"

"Exactly! I don't believe you realize how many times she uses that phrase. Over and over again. She scares people with it. She uses it to make strangers uncomfortable and uneasy. All the time she is saying, 'See! I am not afraid. White Cloud doesn't reject me!'"

"Oh, Flora, that's pretty fanciful."

"She's fanciful. She has a strange imagination, if ever I knew one. But I am sure that behind her wish to use White Cloud to make strangers feel inferior, or unworthy, or something, is some sort of fear of her own. Something scared her."

"Good Lord, Flora——"

"I'm not clever, Niles, but something assures me I am right. I've always known she was frightened about something."

"What did you know about her childhood? Did she ever talk to you about it?"

"Very little. It seemed commonplace enough, and rather poor, I think."

"Yes, I saw that. It was a peculiar little house. It told you nothing at all about the man who lived there. His parishioners respected him. I saw that, too. But no one could tell me much. I never saw a place with so few photographs or papers. Nothing of the stuff that collects through a lifetime. There was a rather extensive-looking family tree. Victoria doesn't seem to pay any attention to that kind of thing in her own family."

"She certainly works on the Grandolets, though."

"Yes, she does."

"Odd, isn't it?"

"It's a peculiar fact that I know as little about Victoria as I did the first day I ever saw her."

"The first day you ever saw her. I guess I shall never forget that day."

"Why?"

Flora looked at him for a full minute. "I see no reason why I shouldn't tell you, though I wonder that you didn't know."

"Flora——"

"It's just that I was so crazily in love with you, Niles."

"Why, Flora——"

"I am still. I shall always be. No, don't say anything. Just let me say it, and then we'll forget that it was said at all. Only——"

"Only what, dear?"

"I wonder what is going to become of us. I hate to see you unhappy, and I hated being unhappy."

Niles leaned forward in his chair. "Flora, you do know, don't you, that I've lived in the north wing of White Cloud ever since Q-G was born?"

"Yes, Niles. I've always known that. I guess it was knowing it that seemed to give me a little right to think about you."

"Long ago, I battled the question out about you."

Flora's round eyes darkened until they looked quite black. "It did have to be settled, Flora."

"But—it was really all settled, anyway, wasn't it?"

"Not necessarily."

"Oh, I don't know, Niles. I suppose I'd have said yes to anything you asked, but, still, I don't know. There's your Grandfather Julien, and Mother, and Aunt Lucie. Somehow I guess I'd have thought what they would have done."

"The Grandolets are impatient people. And now——"

Flora looked startled.

"Now, Flora, things look different."

The color went slowly out of her face. She arose and stood looking into the fire. Then she turned and faced him.

"I'll be everything you wish me to be. Sometimes I hoped you wouldn't ask me, sometimes I could hardly bear that you didn't. That sounds silly and feminine and unreasonable."

He had arisen and was standing close to her.

"Don't misunderstand me, Niles. There was never a day or a night that I didn't want you. There can never be such a day."

Niles placed his hands on her shoulders and kissed her.

"Niles!"

"Yes, dear."

"*Victoria knows.*"

"Knows what?"

"About us."

"But there isn't anything to know about us. We——"

"What we think, what we feel, what—what could happen to us."

"Oh, Flora, after all, Victoria isn't clairvoyant, or a crystal-gazer."

"I don't know."

"Be sensible——"

"How can anyone be sensible here in this lonely river country? We're all touched with it—in one way or another."

"Aren't you taking a cue from Victoria herself?"

"No. She took her cue from us—from the way things are. And she's intuitive, or psychic, or whatever you wish to call it." Flora looked suddenly distraught. "Oh, Niles, Niles——"

He drew her close to him. "What's the matter, Flora?"

"Niles, it's Victoria. She's our enemy, really. She's an enemy of everything we are. She's an enemy of White Cloud!"

"Now, now——"

"I know you don't believe it. You think I'm overwrought or hysterical. I guess I am—overwrought, at least. There has been something in the very air of these places for the past ten years that wears at your nerves, mine, everybody's. Something malevolent, that eats the solid ground out from under us." She controlled her voice with an effort and went on more quietly. "And, Niles, I won't be driven out! I won't go away."

"No one wishes you to, Flora, my dear."

"Yes. *She* does."

"Flora——"

"Wait. Let me speak. It's you and me, from now on. You don't know maybe what's happening—invisibly, to us. I don't either. But it is you and me—together."

"Of course, of course." Niles spoke like a man quieting a child. Flora knew that he did not understand her, but she was relieved, nevertheless, that she had spoken.

"Flora?"

"Yes, Niles."

"I—I suppose we have to set ourselves on a path—we're sort of committed. Listen, Flora darling, I'm not going home tonight."

She was silent for a moment. "I wish it could have been some other way, Niles, but that, too, is something we can't decide, I guess."

Niles caught her to him again, roughly. Then all of the strength went out of her and she turned her face up to his. Presently she drew herself from his arms. "Careful, Niles."

"I can't be careful, forever."

"You don't need to be, really. It's only the servants. I'll tell Atlanta you're staying tonight. The garden room."

Niles' face set. The garden room was a ground-floor room

opening on a small, enclosed formal garden. A stairway outside of its door led to the upper gallery and directly to the windows of Flora's rooms.

"Think twice, Flora. Maybe I'm——"

"Sh! I've thought a thousand times."

"Your mother and Aunt Lucie. Will they think anything?"

Flora laughed. "The old dears. Just a minute, Niles. I'll speak to Atlanta."

Excitement burned in Niles' eyes, but he tried to speak calmly.

"You may hate me for this."

"Never."

"I don't like sneaking."

"I'd face anything, Niles, the world, everybody—the family, even."

He tried to smile. *Even* the family?"

"Yes. Now, wait a minute. I'll be right back."

He marveled at her sudden lightheartedness. Women were unaccountable. Once the dangerous distance between desire and accomplishment is bridged they seem not to look back.

Flora returned presently. She was smiling.

"What are you smiling about?"

"Something irrelevant, maybe."

"What?"

"You know how Victoria has worked at the family legends?"

"Yes, and Grandfather Julien has helped."

"But he hasn't collaborated completely."

"How do you know?"

"I know. It's the story of Far Félice. She has never found out, and your Grandfather Julien, God bless him, couldn't tell her."

"I don't understand. Couldn't tell her what? And how do you know?"

"If Victoria knew, she'd let us know that she knew. She's had only an inkling."

"I still don't know the story myself. You sound as if *you* do. But how do you know what Grandfather Julien said or didn't say?"

"He told me."

"Really? But, of course, I think he loves you above everything."

"I don't know. I hope so. But the story: he said he told her it wasn't clear, and probably wasn't true, and that anything any of us had heard was better forgotten. And then he just stared at me, without blinking, you know the way he does."

"But you know the story, or whatever, about Far Félice?"

"Yes. And I'm the only one who does know the whole truth of it."

"Oh, Lord, Flora, are *you* going to be mysterious, too?"

"No. I had planned to tell you all about it. The details had been forgotten. There are only rumors. Apparently the Grandolets and the Vélazys and others for once in their lives managed to keep a secret. And then with the passing of a generation it was all but forgotten."

Niles frowned. "I remember this much—I mean I heard this much: Quintin and his brother Paul quarreled and fought and killed each other, and somehow the library caught fire——"

"Do you remember what they quarreled about?"

"Does anyone know? They were both dead."

"Try. Don't you recall, or did you never hear?"

"But how does anyone know, positively? No one was present—or so I heard."

"No one was present. But it was a long quarrel. It was about Quintin's wife."

"I had *heard* that, of course."

"There were reasons, maybe."

"What's the mystery? Tell me about it."

"You do remember who Quintin's wife was?"

"Yes, of course. Jeannette Vélazy!"

"Yes."

"A close-in fight. Listen, *was* there a scandal, or what?"

"Yes. The Grandolets faced the world foursquare, afterward."

"They always do in trouble, don't they?"

"But there was actually a question of paternity, Niles."

"Good God! Really?" He laughed shortly. "I told you the Grandolets were not always patient people."

"Nor the Vélazys, it seems."

"We're all the same. But—oh, good Lord, Flora, do you mean Grandfather Julien——"

"The story is that there was doubt whose child he was. It seems that Quintin drove Jeannette nearly crazy with his continual inquisition, and she killed herself."

"So she did. I recall that much now. What a ghastly mess that must have been!"

"Quintin regarded her suicide as an admission of guilt, and summoned Paul. You know the rest."

"Then no one really *does* know?"

"Niles, here is the characteristic part of the story! There were challenges right and left, but the Grandolets and the Vélazys got together somehow in a family council and declared the story was false and that there were no grounds for suspicion. As I said, they faced the whole thing down. They almost convinced the outside world that the deaths of Quintin and Paul were accidental!"

"I wish I could have seen that conclave! Imagine it!"

"You see a lot was involved."

"What else?"

"Property."

"Oh, oh, of course. If Grandfather Julien—I can't even say the word, Flora!"

"It seems that if he could have been declared the son of Paul, he would not have inherited White Cloud. White Cloud was just being finished then. White Cloud lands, you know, had been Jeannette's dowry. The house was built, of course, by Quintin. I guess it would have been right much mixed up, anyway."

"Wait a minute! Let me get this clear. Why, why—White Cloud today would belong to your brother Louis, wouldn't it?"

"I think so."

"White Cloud——" Niles looked strangely haggard. He looked past Flora, wide-eyed and unseeing. "White Cloud," he repeated.

"Oh, for heaven's sake, Niles! White Cloud is **not really in-**volved. It's a dead and forgotten story."

"Yes, the family council decided—arbitrarily."

"Not quite."

"Why 'not quite'?"

"The principal support of the dead Jeannette Vélazy was her personal maid, Jubilee."

"What a name! I never heard of her."

"She was Orlou's grandmother."

"Good Lord! No wonder——"

"What?"

"Orlou's been like one of the family, more so than is usual even in the case of an extraordinary servant. So was her mother before her."

"Yes, I imagine so."

"Flora, I'd be willing to bet anything that if any soul on earth knows that old story, the truth of it, it is Orlou."

"I shouldn't be surprised. But no one will ever find it out from her. No one can. But can't you see how even Julien is unwilling that any hint of the story should come to Victoria?"

"Y-yes, I guess so."

"Julien doesn't trust anyone that far. That's family, Niles."

"Good Lord! Maybe we've been wearing a nice invisible bar sinister all of these years!"

"Don't be silly, Niles. I don't believe a word of it."

"You don't? Well, why?"

"I don't know. I just know." She spoke airily, and smiled her dimpled, childish smile.

Niles looked helpless. "Fine old family intuition, I guess, eh?"

"Maybe. Though, actually, I can't see that it would have made or could have made any difference."

Niles roared. "Flora, you're wonderful! Just so it's all in the family?"

She nodded. "Quintin and Paul were twins, even!" Then she smiled brightly, as if she had explained away all the difficulties of a century.

"I don't know what I could possibly do without you, darling." Niles sounded serious, but an amused look lingered in his eyes.

Flora looked thoughtfully at the rosy tips of her fingers. "I think you are making fun of me."

"Far from it. Far, far from it."

"I've been thinking a lot about our families these past years. First of all, I couldn't help it with Mama and Aunt Lucie about. All of the endless sifting and sorting of family stories used to buzz past my ears. But I think it was actually Victoria's spooky talk that set me to thinking, and to asking what we really are. I've been trying to answer for myself the same questions that seem to bother her so much."

"Have you found out yet?"

"In a way, yes. It's sort of annoying at first trying to pin down anything tangible. Take you, for example. So many people say you are a 'typical Grandolet,' a 'real old-time Grandolet.' But how little old-time Grandolet blood have you? Your mother was a Tennessee girl, a Lacey, your grandmother——"

"The old war horse, Isabella."

"Yes, and so on back, and back. You seem to be everything but 'Grandolet.'"

"Well, darling, we're talking usually about a single tradition that has become identified with a family."

"But why? Why is one tradition stronger than another?"

"You tell me."

"What happens when a Grandolet collides with a Vélazy?"

"Maybe the tradition changes without our knowing it."

"I don't think so. There is some kind of little thread that keeps growing stronger and stronger——"

"Or a wall that everyone adds a brick to until we can't see over it."

"You won't be serious."

"I don't want to be philosophical. But I do want to know something."

"Yes. What?"

"How do you happen to know the story of Far Félice so well?"

"I was wondering when you'd ask that simple little question. There's a simple little answer. I've done some research in family history myself."

"Papers? Letters?"

"Yes. There was a lot of stuff in the New Orleans house that I thought I'd better bring to Wyandotte. I—I thought this was going to be home."

"Isn't it?"

"Now, yes, and forever."

He moved nearer to her and laid his hand over hers. "As you said, it's you and me, from now on."

"Let me tell you. There was one letter which evidently Lorain Vélazy was to have destroyed, but didn't. It was from his brother, Bernard Vélazy, and was written at Far Félice."

"Yes?"

"It was written immediately after the notable family council I told you about just now. Lorain, apparently, was ill and couldn't come up to Far Félice, but Bernard did go, and was making due report of the proceedings."

"You have the letter?"

"Yes. It is, I imagine, the only written record there is. I've saved it for you. I don't know why. I imagined that since I—one Vélazy here in the twentieth century—had discovered the story, one Grandolet should know. I thought of Julien first, and then decided it must be you."

"Is there something in it I *ought* to know?"

"Really no more than I've told you, except that it is an illustration of that bond which has held us all together, whether we understand what it is or not."

"Far Félice." Niles said the name musingly.

"Far Félice seems to be the dark side of us, doesn't it? This story would sort of establish that. Maybe that's why it was finally abandoned for White Cloud. Just left behind with the old dead secrets—dead as the people to whom they were once important. But this one——"

"What about it?"

"It might just turn out to be important if Victoria found it. It's between us, Niles. I'll give you the letter. You can read it; then, I think, it should be destroyed."

That evening after supper, Niles drew a chair close to the crackling fire. The garden room felt damp, and he closed the curtains over the tall glass doors. A slow rain was falling outside.

The letter was written on small sheets of blue paper in a tight, meticulous hand. It was in French and Niles had to read slowly.

Dear Lorain:

I have been at Far Félice for a week, and these days have been exciting and interesting almost beyond description. There are many details of my visit here, informations and anecdotes about our numerous cousins that I must relate to you more fully when I see you again.

The journey here was most tiresome. The heat was extreme, and the mosquitoes a torture. I can assure you that I was delighted when the boat finally reached the Far Félice landing. I found a considerable gathering of the family, all men of course. Great Uncle Fabien, quite venerable now, but surprisingly agile of body and alert of mind, agreed with Auguste and Gaillard Grandolet that these matters could not be freely discussed in the presence of the ladies, and that masculine judgment would, in any event, be more free of prejudice and more amenable to the principles of reason. And this, as you will see, was quite true.

There was considerable stiffness at first, as you can imagine. It would have seemed most comical to you, my dear Lorain, if you could have seen the rigid backs and the short little bows all around. The Grandolets, proud as the devil always, and our own people infallibly courteous. No one was willing that any other should show greater courtesy than he. This amiable rivalry, I may say, probably prevented the outbreak of further hostilities. There were occasional moments when I felt certain that even the restraints of good manners would not be able to withstand the acute strain.

I think the difficult situations were greatly relieved on the day Philippe Ronsard d'Aupais arrived. Of course, you know he never forgave the family for its treatment of his uncle Hippolyte. You may imagine to yourself our astonishment when he had himself announced, *announced,* mind you, at the drawing-room door as M. Philippe Ronsard *Grandolet!* Everyone arose with extraordinary promptitude, and there was even a murmur of applause. Certainly all of us understood. Philippe had come with a new spirit of forgiveness and good will, and by his amiable resumption of the family name gave the first impulse to family unity. It was most agreeable, and all of us felt a sudden refreshment of spirit and a strengthening of good resolution.

You know of course all of the regrettable and melancholy events that led to this assembly. Old Fabien, with the greatest fortitude, reviewed the whole sad history. It was a somewhat legalistic procedure and spared no one. He did not even hesitate to resurrect the ancient history of Cristine Vélazy and LeRoy Grandolet, which is indeed a page of our family record that is of even less credit to the Vélazys than the Grandolets. He concluded by saying quite solemnly,

Qu'heureux est celui dont la transgression est quittée, duquel le péché est couvert.

Do you not think this was most curious? I may say that I was sure most of the Vélazys were not too well pleased, since the assumption was inescapable that there was of a truth sin to be covered!

The entire story was discussed with more frankness than I would have considered possible. On the second day (we began our deliberations on Wednesday afternoon) Fabien called in Jeannette's maid, Jubilee. It appeared to all of us that he exhibited courage in doing so. It was actually calling upon the word of a slave to contradict the fears and beliefs and accusations of the Grandolets. But in that moment Fabien did truly measure to formidable stature. He said quite simply: "We may rest our confidence on the belief of this faithful servant in her mistress Jeannette Vélazy Grandolet." By using both names he seemed to close over the family schism with one happy phrase. It was both an overture of good will and a conclusion of amity. Then he added this unbelievable word. "I think we may accept the assurances of Jubilee, who has devoted herself so unselfishly to both our families, all the more that she is, in the humble way of her kind, *one of us.*" I may tell you that if the Vélazys had murmured before at mention of Cristine, the Grandolets almost leapt from their chairs at this. But Fabien only held up his hand and said, tranquilly: "Wherefore?"

And, truly, who of us has much to say in this instance?

The woman Jubilee did rather put a face of shame on us. It was without bitterness that a resurgence of chivalry came to all of us.

The short of it is that it was solemnly agreed that no stain of doubt rested upon the name of Jeannette Vélazy, and that no question could be raised now or forever concerning the rights of Jeannette's infant Julien. We parted upon this felicitous and harmonious conclusion. There is no question now of White Cloud. It is firmly the legacy of little Julien, who I may say is a most beautiful child.

In confidence to you, I may add, that there were many discussions on the side. We had met and we had told the world what we thought that all future scandal may be forever quieted, but there were those among us there who remembered the austerity of Quintin Grandolet, and the reckless deviltry of his contrasting twin brother Paul. Nor could we be entirely oblivious of the warm and passionate nature of our cousin Jeannette. So, after all, who knows?

It is enough that we have essayed to preserve our family traditions, and have in such good measure succeeded in doing so.

I drove down to see the new house. It is appropriately named White Cloud. It is a noble house, and though not quite finished will make a most suitable residence for young Julien.

I expect to return home by easy stages. I must make a visit to see Aunt Celeste. She is now past ninety and in full possession of her faculties, I am told. I should be able to rejoin you within the month and I shall have many amusing details to recount which I do not deem the part of wisdom to commit to paper.

Your faithful brother

BERNARD

I think this epistle should be destroyed at once. There was an unspoken agreement among us that all details of our considerations were to be scrupulously guarded from repetition. I have written you only that you may be properly informed.

B. V.

Niles folded the letter and then laid it on the bed of coals. The fragile paper flared for an instant and then the lamentable story of Jeannette Vélazy and the Grandolet twins was ashes.

The little mantel clock chimed eleven. The rain had stopped and the house was silent. He cupped his hand about the lamp chimney and blew out the light. In the faint glow from the fire he felt his way to the door, went out, and up the narrow stairs to the upper gallery.

Victoria clipped her papers carefully together. She had been writing and this unexpected exercise of her mind had given her a surprising pleasure. She was wondering now if it might not be an interesting pursuit to compose sketches of all the family personalities. One could surmise much that did not appear in records, one could fill in from imagination, and guess at much more.

Flora's observation that the family personality "bothered" Victoria was shrewdly correct. Victoria had said often to herself, I am a Grandolet, but she had come again, as in the beginning, to find herself outside. To break an entrance to that composite of strangely associated qualities, views, temperaments, wills, aspirations, and mockeries seemed impossible. She felt often as if she groped about the base of a tower which showed neither window nor door.

She arose and went out on the gallery. Q-G was playing on top of the levee with a half-dozen little pickaninnies. The sound of his commanding voice came clear and shrill across the garden. Victoria puckered her brow a little as she thought of Q-G. How easily and completely Q-G entered into what was family—no, he did not enter, he *was*. And how curiously even he looked at her sometimes, as if he did not understand her because she was a stranger.

"Miss Victoria."

"Yes, Pinky?"

"Here's a letter for you."

"Thank you."

She opened the square buff envelope. That was Cousin Paula's handwriting. The letter was a chatty, gossipy, rambling story of Paula's recent visit to New Orleans. Paula was a faraway cousin who lived at Oquipah. A postscript was crowded about the margin of the last page.

We are all greatly grieved over the death of Dr. Cheer. A new doctor, rather young, has come to take his place. His name is Lawrence Gaynes. He has a charming wife. Most of us feel that no one can take the place of Dr. Cheer. I have just decided for myself that I won't be sick!

P. G.

She placed the letter in the pocket of her smock. Q-G and his black safari had disappeared. She descended the steps, crossed the gardens aimlessly, and went up to the levee. The river was high. The yellow flow covered the swamp. She could tell by the rim of debris pushed in to the edge that the water was still rising.

FIFTEEN

MANY TIMES DURING the ensuing months Victoria had bitter cause to remember that quiet afternoon. That day she had been secure in herself. She had been alone as she wished to be upon her self-appointed road. How soon had come the revelation that she was no longer alone, that she was fearfully accompanied, and that every agonized nerve rebelled, acquiesced, fought, surrendered, and mocked what she had believed was her own inviolable peace.

Dr. Lawrence Gaynes came, at Niles' invitation, to be introduced, and to see White Cloud. He came for a Saturday-to-Monday week end and brought his wife.

Dr. Gaynes was a quiet man. One could not say at once if he were shy or merely silent and observant. He was rather slight and had nothing of a professional manner about him. Victoria thought he looked like an actor. There was a quick play of expression on his face, and his thin, long-fingered hands sketched a lively commentary to his brief and picturesque comments.

"You aren't French, Dr. Gaynes? Your name——"

"I had a French grandmother. I hope I resemble her."

"It was only your name."

Mrs. Gaynes, blonde, placid, and realistic of eye, nodded understandingly. "I know. It's Lawrence's gestures that give him away, don't you think?"

The conversation that first evening stayed comfortably in conventional channels. Dinner was impressive. Victoria had a talent for making the most commonplace event seem important. Niles glanced at her several times during that dinner with reluctant approval. She had improved on the old Grandolet entertaining which used to be stiff or lazily casual.

Dr. Gaynes was enthusiastic about White Cloud. Coming out from the dining room he had stopped and given a prolonged boyish whistle.

"It's stunning, isn't it? Look at those galleries, Marian. They look like something flying. Excuse me, Mrs. Grandolet, but I must comment. I know a lot of Louisiana houses, but this is unique, isn't it?"

"I don't know, Dr. Gaynes. I have not seen many. I think you might like Far Félice as much as this."

"Oh, I've heard about what you are doing up there. It is *up,* isn't it? I hear you even have a couple of good ghosts."

Victoria smiled gravely. "All old houses have them."

"Even White Cloud?"

Niles and the rest of the company had gone on to the drawing room. Victoria looked questioningly at him.

"I'm not sure I should answer."

"Oh, I wasn't serious."

"Maybe it is a serious question." She hesitated for a moment. "Yes, I rather think I'd say White Cloud has its ghosts."

"Really?"

She turned suddenly. "Come up to the first gallery with me."

Dr. Gaynes laughed. "You haven't ghosts on tap, have you?"

"I—I think perhaps the real ones are always present." Victoria spoke in a low voice, a shade tensely. The effect on Dr. Gaynes was noticeable.

On the stairs she stopped and looked up at the chandelier. "It was brought from Scotland by a traveling Grandolet, early in the nineteenth century. It is never still—never."

"Interesting. It does seem—er—quite alive, doesn't it?"

"Yes."

"Rather malevolently alive, if one wished to be fanciful."

"No, no, not exactly. Just watchful. Come."

"Oh, your picture gallery. This is most interesting. Dead and gone Grandolets, I see."

"I wonder if anyone ever really dies here. You say 'dead and gone'—it's the usual phrase, isn't it? Dr. Gaynes, at White Cloud the dead are very much with us."

Dr. Gaynes looked slightly bewildered for a second, then he smiled and entered instantly into the spirit of her talk. He was a subtler man than Victoria guessed. He was interested to see how far she could carry that sort of thing.

"I want to take you to a—a certain spot here on this gallery."

He watched her with open admiration. A really beautiful woman, he thought, with the kind of mind that amazingly matched her unique and arresting appearance.

Victoria was looking her best. Her hair was satin smooth and coiled close about her head. She wore a bluish-gray chiffon dress that seemed to envelop her in a cloud. It nearly matched and emphasized her smoky gray-blue eyes. Her clear pallor, her meticulous grooming, and her extreme daintiness combined to make her at once remote and utterly alluring.

"Here. Here by this column."

She stopped, and Dr. Gaynes looked about him.

"Here?"

"Yes."

"Am I supposed to see something?"

"No. Listen."

He turned his head but his eyes were on her face.

"I'm sorry." He smiled apologetically.

"Wait a moment. Listen."

And suddenly he did hear what she wished him to hear. A faint rustling sound like the frou-frou of silk, and then the elusive, quick, multiple whisper.

"Jove! That *is* interesting, isn't it?"

She smiled one-sidedly. Her slight shrug suggested that she no longer thought of the phenomenon as interesting.

The whisper rose and sank, died away, and sounded again from another direction. Dr. Gaynes stepped back and surveyed the circular galleries.

"*Very* interesting. An acoustical freak, of course."

Again she smiled, and precisely repeated Niles' characteristic gesture of a combined shrug, smile, and lift of eyebrows.

"I don't know, Dr. Gaynes."

"Oh, but, really, it couldn't be anything else."

"I don't know. I am, after all, just a simple country woman. After a long time these houses become more than just houses. They are perhaps saturated through and through with the life that has been here. I—I don't know, one can't always be clear about what is happening. Oh, what I mean to say is that we who live so far out of the world find ourselves perhaps closer to out-of-the-world things."

"But manifestations——"

She stopped him with a playful lift of her hand.

"I know what you are going to say, but, you see, it is difficult after a while to know which are the familiar happenings of an everyday world, and—which are not."

"There's a little danger on that road, Mrs. Grandolet."

She did not meet his suddenly keen professional scrutiny.

"I fancy there are many times when we are on the border line of the—oh, I don't like to say *the unknown*—perhaps you do know what I mean. Certainly you can't be so realistic or so materialistic that you believe only in what we see."

"No, Mrs. Grandolet. My practice compels me to believe in the power of a lot of things we can't see, but I don't necessarily believe in their reality."

"Oh, dear! This sounds metaphysical. Let's go up to the roof. You must see my garden."

"Roof garden?"

"Yes." She stopped and looked up. "You see, there was once a sort of fourth half story on the house, but the floor was removed and it was left like that to light the galleries."

"Oh, a belvedere."

"Yes. As it is now, you see it's a sort of—what would you say? It isn't a dome since it's square."

"I'd still call it a belvedere, I suppose."

"Well, anyway, in warm weather all of those windows can be opened from the outside to let hot air escape from the house."

"I see."

She was suddenly gay and chatty. "Do you know, I've never been able to find out if belvedere was the half story itself, or the wide promenade around it. But it is lovely up there."

They reached a narrow stair that arose from the very edge of the top gallery.

"Don't look over, it will make you dizzy."

They came out on the roof. The area had been set with potted plants and there were a dozen white wrought-iron chairs.

"Charming, Mrs. Grandolet, charming."

"The view is really fine. The great curve of the river, and then back here you look out across the treetops."

"Dark out that way, too, isn't it?"

A flood of moonlight silvered the trees and the intricate roof structure of the house with an utter magic.

Victoria stood looking toward the distant, black mass of trees.

"I always feel that we've pushed it back—just for a little while. It keeps coming back. Every minute all that savage wilderness creeps toward us. Only watchfulness——"

"Yes, that's true of all man's place."

"But it's so immediate here. The swamps and bayous back there, the river before us. White Cloud stands like—like a momentary and beautiful pause between them."

"You're rather a poet, Mrs. Grandolet."

"No, no. I came here a stranger, and—I see."

Dr. Gaynes' open touring car was often seen at White Cloud. Sometimes Mrs. Gaynes came, but more often the doctor came alone. He was tremendously interested in White Cloud and its traditions and, later on, in Victoria's interpretations of the moods and atmosphere of the house.

"I rather think," Victoria remarked, "that such houses are first naturally and simply the product of a period and a way of thinking."

"We-ell, superficially of a period, but in the individual house, surprisingly, they are the visible signals of a way of thinking."

"Aren't you talking about the atmosphere of a house created after it is built, by the people who live in it?"

"No, and I think you know better than I do what I am talking about. Houses are among the strangest creations of man, the most revealing, and, in the long run, factors having profound influence on the dwellers."

"You do think so?"

"In a psychological sense, yes. You think so, too."

"Of course."

"I'm curious about White Cloud—and you."

Victoria looked startled. "Why? How?"

"It's a powerful sort of place, isn't it?"

"I suppose so. I am used to it, naturally." She sounded indifferent, but Dr. Gaynes knew she was suddenly excited.

"Maybe this is impertinent, but, you see, I didn't know you when you came here, and——"

"I was very young."

"And so I don't completely know what it has done to you."

"Isn't it rather fanciful to suppose that one is radically or deeply influenced by a mere house?"

"You are fencing. White Cloud isn't a mere house. Its setting alone is remarkable—that river out there, that huge, indifferent, savage river, and the picturesque, old-world gardens here at your door, the violent, threatening quality of nature in this region—everything is keyed pretty high, Victoria. The house, well, that is the spirit of the Grandolets somehow. All of these old places have that strong historic feel, as if they'd been witnesses of high tragedy."

"They have. But you're reading that in."

"Not entirely. The pride, and if you'll forgive the word, the insolence expressed in what most of you call these gracious houses were in themselves a revelation of the certain end results."

"You make an interesting mixture of poetry and socialism, Lawrence."

"I don't know about the poetry, but I'm sure of the socialism.

Certain orders of society are doomed by their natures, and that is neither an original nor a profound comment. It's just so."

"It wouldn't be a popular idea with the Grandolets, I fancy."

"But you're a Grandolet yourself."

"No. My son is a Grandolet. But there is always one person in these intensely ingrown families who is alien and an observer."

"Yes, I see. But you became——"

"Like Isabella Niles up there." She gestured toward the portrait, and smiled a bit sarcastically. "The grandest Grandolet of them all."

"We're getting off the track. There's a new psychology coming up, Victoria, and it's going to throw a lot of light on our insides. It has already."

"Like that book you lent me?"

"Yes."

"I couldn't read it."

"Didn't want to, you mean. Shocked?"

"Yes."

"That's funny. Victoria, back to this house. Defenseless creatures in the wilderness take on protective coloring. People do, too."

"Defenseless?"

"Most of us are defenseless against what we don't know, or see, or understand. Our subconscious minds take alarm and help us to hide. I'd rather call it our secret mind, because I'm sure it is the same mind working in the dark."

"You're bringing a new ghost to White Cloud, Lawrence."

"Oh, we're full of them, ourselves, and usually carry them with us."

There was more and more of this kind of talk. It amused

Dr. Gaynes to see Victoria caught by the trite and melodramatic aspects of new speculations. She interested him, he thought, as a case. He saw that she was disturbed and defensive. He wondered a good deal, but it was difficult to classify her. So much of what she seemed to reveal impulsively was patently calculated and arranged. It was not always possible to sort out the truth from pretense.

He and Victoria visited Wyandotte often, but Victoria always created the impression there that they had only stopped for a moment in some progress of greater interest and importance. They went much to Far Félice. Its especial atmosphere brought up more and more discussion.

Dr. Gaynes was not as detached as he believed himself to be, but neither was he off guard. He saw clearly at Wyandotte that Victoria was making a quiet parade of him, partly as a friend who understood deep things, partly as a sort of conquest. And it was in that second aspect that she irritated him. She left too much the impression that this was, oh, certainly, a conquest, but a conquest which she accepted as a readily understandable situation, but one in which she gave nothing.

Dr. Gaynes wondered with a mixture of amusement and exasperation how she contrived to expose just that delicate balance in which she kept for herself the maximum of safety. He decided that perhaps he could play, too. She was a lovely and alluring person. She did stir his senses more than a little, and if it should turn out as such things often did, well——He did not think of Marian at such times. Victoria accomplished one thing which he did not fully measure. She had a talent for making other women seem extremely obvious. And, because she achieved a dramatic kind of conversation as a regular performance, Dr. Gaynes fell into the easy habit of being artificially interesting and dramatic. It made a stimulating sort of exchange—rather as if they were rehearsing a play.

Soon Far Félice became a stage on which they more or less consciously acted what they enjoyed as picturesque roles—roles with a constant undertone of tragic implications.

The place and the parts they played gratified a lingering adolescence in Victoria. It was a delayed payment for some very early denials.

She cleverly recognized it as being precisely that, but she was not at all sure that this was true of Lawrence. She was pleased with the thought that it might not be true, that he was making himself really another feature of her dramatization of herself. He fitted well into the background of Far Félice. She liked to see him there. She told him so, and it pleased him.

Victoria knew before long that their continued close companionship was being talked about. She saw the hostile look of appraisal and dismay in Mrs. Gaynes' eyes, and was content. She saw Flora and Aunt Lucie and Marie Vélazy watching her, and a hard defiance grew in her.

But Niles disconcerted her. He seemed to be secretly smiling, secretly mocking, and immeasurably detached. It aroused something correspondingly mocking in her, but—she was not quite able to match his amused detachment. Victoria had played life with heavy accents; she could not achieve that kind of lightness. Moreover, she knew she was in danger—oh, not from Niles, or anyone outside—she was in danger from herself. This was not going to be a scandal. It was a divertissement, and heaven knows she deserved to have that much. She told herself that Lawrence might guard himself as best he could, that was really no concern of hers. But she was fond of him. He supplied something.

And then, all at once, she knew she was more than fond of Lawrence Gaynes. The knowledge and the fact came to her with staggering violence.

Victoria thought hard. She had seen the river break through its barriers in just this way. The whole mighty flood, with its stupendous might sweeping past, safely held, appearing to be no more than a spectacle. She had watched it, thrilled with its hurtling power. She had seen the smallest break widen with an increasing rush, and then the disaster that tore away the very contours of the landscape.

Everything unawakened in Victoria, everything repressed and denied in her nature, sprang into an intense and morbid life. It was like a hurricane.

She turned her face away from it as best she could. She was unable actually to believe her own nerves and the insistence of her own mind. She had always been cool, she had always stood at a safe distance from anything like an invasion of her own personality, she had been proud of her own aloofness. She had taken that pride in her solitariness as a matter of course, as a personal and peculiar possession, a distinguishing endowment. She, Victoria Grandolet.

Daily, hourly, she had to meet the stranger within herself. She was forced to look upon herself there in her "secret mind" agonized by a sense of her outraged immunity.

The hateful, physical facts of her sudden obsession were the hardest facts of all for her to sustain. She had never liked to touch anyone or to be touched. She had shut away from any recognition every memory of those first few months when Niles shared her room and her bed. She had sealed the memory darkly from consciousness until, when she thought of it at all, she found the memory dim and unreal as a dream recalled with difficulty in the full light of day.

She recoiled with a half horror from what her senses were frankly and brutally demanding. She recoiled, retreated, and came again helpless to her own torment with the lash of starvation sharp upon her.

Victoria fought, but she was not fighting for any convention because her mind had never accepted a convention. Conventions—they were the checks which one applied to others for one's own convenience. The forms of honor, even, were but the comfortable passages from situations of discomfort. She had always used such things as shields between herself and the unwelcome importunities of either the conventional or the unconventional. No, she was not fighting for anything that other people fought for. She was fighting for the recovery of her accustomed cool volition, for the simple possession of herself.

But she was losing, not merely this simple possession of her will, she was losing what Orlou had long ago called what is and what is not. And with that irrecoverable loss went all of those same measures of proportion.

Out here you have to measure things by a great big sky, against the woods, or against the river itself. It's not human and you forget to think like a human.

She had lost that measure. Something had arisen out of the deeps of her own flesh, the common, ordinary demand of fulfillment, and it had arisen to grotesque stature; it filled her mind and her world, it clamored at her brain and distorted the simple clarity of everything that lay about her.

When you have people around you, you can always measure things by them . . . You can think and dream yourself out of this world. First thing you don't know what is what or what's alive and what's dead.

No, no, no! Orlou was wrong. She had not had many people about her, that was true, but also, she had not wanted them.

And was it not true that she had not been able to take any reckoning of her own imaginative spirit and nature against those who came and went at White Cloud? There had been no one—until Lawrence came. Lawrence! She felt herself being drawn—down and down, drowned in this deadly undertow of passion.

One frightening thought crossed and recrossed her turbulent attention. How did Lawrence feel? What was she to him? He had never said. Oh, yes, there had been all of that fine talk at Far Félice. She looked back through those days to see herself with a hideous clarity. She had been acting. Could he have been doing the same thing? What if he meant no more in all of that brilliant exchange than she had meant? Had he awakened from a sort of rehearsal to find that the play was real? And if he had not, could she bring him to face the blinding truth?

Now when she met him she fell back upon the only remaining pitiful shard of her broken pride. She was not sure that she could deceive him: he knew her well. Suppose he saw but did not respond. She rejected that—that thought impossible beyond all impossible thoughts.

She held as tight as she could. She was Victoria Grandolet. She was mistress of White Cloud. Nothing must be jeopardized. She must be careful—careful that she did not play away all of the treasure of her gains. She was no ordinary woman. She would not be an ordinary woman.

Far Félice in her mind arose now to its full and competent power. The place was always in her mind. White Cloud had become almost unbearable. Far Félice was her own. She experienced an increased liberation there, and a sort of assurance.

Victoria struggled to establish a clear order in her mind. She tried to make plans—for herself, for anything that would create a firm foothold in her slippery insecurity. She spent hours in the little sitting room, demanding almost of Isabella Niles' portrait the strength to reach out and still the tumult that circled dizzily about her. She had looked so often and so long at Isabella that she built into her self-estimate a belief in their real community. But it was not Isabella who asserted her old strength of suggestion and made herself an almost palpable presence. It was not Isabella whose imperious glance bore resolution across the yawning past to the sentient present. No: it was Hippolyte d'Aupais, smiling, insouciant, mocking, and no less despotic in his insinuant charges than Isabella herself.

"He had his cake and ate it, too." Niles had said that, whether in contempt or envious approval she had not been able to decide.

Victoria resented the vulgar proverb. But from her own long thinking of Hippolyte came back an insistently repeated echo.

He had what he wanted.

He had what he wanted.

Hippolyte d'Aupais not only had what he wanted, but came back to live in a sunny peace at Far Félice. Could anyone say he slept less well than Isabella up there in his tomb at Far Félice?

And now, after all these years had run away, no one pronounced blame at sight of that unquenchable smile. Not at all. They spoke warmly of him, almost tenderly, and with an emotion shading beyond reluctant admiration. The Grandolets, the Vélazys, and all the kin, distant and near, treasured him. One could not help but believe he represented to all of them the realization of their own denials and frustrations. Yes, but certainly, Hippolyte d'Aupais had about what he wanted, and his portrait hung there today—the beloved ancestor.

Victoria's smile wavered, superior and contemptuous.

"The strong and the weak," she said in a whisper. She was not sure what she meant by that, or if she meant anything at all, but a comfortable sense of release rested in her breast for a moment. It was like the release and relief following a difficult decision.

"Marie, I am terrified, simply terrified, by the whole thing." Aunt Lucie held her needle at arm's length, tried to thread it, gave it up, and picked up a palmetto fan. She rocked and fanned herself for a minute or two, laid the fan aside, and looked in her sewing box for a needle with a larger eye. "It seems to me they make very impractical needles nowadays."

"You need new glasses. Here, try this. They call it a self-threader. I'll show you. Why are you terrified?"

"That Victoria will precipitate a scandal."

"There is already a scandal."

"It's about the last thing I thought she would do."

"Are you surprised?"

"Yes."

"She hasn't been living with Niles all these years. You know that."

Aunt Lucie bent over her sewing. "Oh, Marie, I don't like to talk about such things."

"Nothing is surprising coming out of an unnatural situation like that. What do you suppose is the matter with her?"

"I don't know."

"It's unhealthy."

"I can't help but blame Niles—a little."

"For what? If she didn't want him——"

"Oh, dear, no. I don't mean anything like that. I can't imagine Niles being so——"

"Were you going to say *indelicate?*"

[247]

"What makes you think I was?"

"Because it sounds just like you. I blame Niles, too. She should have had six children whether she wanted them or not."

"I was thinking, rather, of this Dr. Gaynes."

"Oh, you want him shot, I suppose?"

Aunt Lucie looked away thoughtfully. "Ye-es. If necessary."

"You're old-fashioned, Lucie. It seems men don't shoot each other nowadays."

"I dare say the Grandolets haven't changed to that extent."

"But Niles doesn't care, Lucie. You know that."

"It isn't that. We can't have a family scandal."

"We've had 'em before, and survived. There was the affair at Far Félice."

"Oh, nobody ever knew the straight of that, I fancy. Anyway, it was all cleared up, wasn't it?"

Marie Vélazy gazed soberly at Aunt Lucie. "Yes," she said quietly. "I believe it was."

"Niles doesn't even look as if he knew anything is going on."

"Well, what is going on? Do you know?"

"Plenty—I assume."

"Lucie, I don't really know much about human passions. People like you and me don't. But, after all, one does read."

"Oh—books!"

Marie disregarded this contemptuous dismissal. "I can imagine that it is possible to find yourself in trouble—in trouble with your emotions before you know it."

"Any woman of breeding——"

"Nothing to do with it, nothing at all." She polished her lorgnettes absently. "I remember once walking out there on that levee when it was new. The river was up and everybody was watching for a break. I was with Julien. We were standing on what seemed solid ground. We made a step or two forward, and the earth seemed to turn to jelly. Water had seeped into it. It looked the same, but it wasn't. We barely pulled ourselves out. And the break came right at that spot."

"I don't know what you are talking about."

"I'm talking about life, Lucie, something neither you nor I know much about. I can imagine, however, that things could be like that. You could believe you had solid ground under your feet, and all at once you sink."

"That sounds fine and dramatic, but I think it is making excuses. One is a lady or one isn't."

"You think that is all there is to it?"

"Yes."

"I wish life were really that simple."

"Are you condoning Victoria's reprehensible behavior?"

"Dear, no. No, indeed, Lucie. I knew from the first she wasn't our kind."

Lucie laughed.

Victoria stood in her downstairs living room. She was leaning against the wall as if something had forced her back against it. She had been trying to think, trying to set some sort of order in her brain, trying to summon her familiar calculating faculties to her aid. For one absurd moment she recalled an old newspaper illustration she had seen many years ago. It was the picture of a child standing against a wall with angry flood waters rushing in from all sides. Just now she felt precisely so placed. And then she thrust the melodramatic thought away. She was not hemmed in, not at all. She was driven by something. She tried to reject the idea of her own emotions possessing any such power over her. One had only to turn this way or that, to say yes or no, to direct or to deny. One might feel—

yes, yes, yes, as she was feeling now, parched and devoured with a passion that she hated while she could not refuse it or put it away from her. But beyond that demanding passion in which her flesh now clamored for its belated fulfillment, beyond that was a still more desperate urgency. She must go on, and on, and on, because of something else deeper than the hunger in her blood.

She looked up at the laughing face of Hippolyte d'Aupais.

I had everything I wanted . . .
I had everything I wanted . . .
I had everything I wanted . . .

Her old thought of him arose in her brain like a chant. It sang in her ears, and beat about her, and died away in a whispering insistence.

She tried to think of him. Had he been really troubled, ever, or had he reached out for what he wanted as simply as he would have reached for a ripe fruit at his hand?

I had everything I wanted . . .
I had everything I wanted . . .

It began again, and then she remembered a voice, fantastically high and thin, singing. That day at Far Félice, the first time she went there.

If I had my way, oh Lawdy, Lawdy,
If I had my way, oh Lawdy, Lawdy,
I'd tear the building down.

She went hurriedly upstairs. She had to escape that room and Hippolyte d'Aupais. She tried to say coldly to herself that she had dramatized too well. She had tried to make something alive, something symbolic of Hippolyte, and he had come alive. There was a hideous magic in him—in this house—

in the whole accursed business of the Grandolets.

She looked steadily at herself in the mirror. She could always bring herself to her senses that way.

"Miss Victoria."

"Yes, Orlou."

"The doctor is downstairs. He wants to know if you want to ride up to Far Félice."

"Why, yes. I think I do."

"You want to change your dress?"

"No, this will do."

"Miss Victoria——"

"What is it, Orlou?"

"I was just thinking of stepping up to Far Félice myself. Could I ride along in the back seat?"

"Why—why, of course. But why are you going to Far Félice today?"

"Greenwood's mother is sort of poorly. I've been thinking I'd better see her."

"Phelia? I hadn't heard she was sick."

"Yes'm, she's sick."

Victoria turned away and smiled a little. She understood, and she was disturbed because she knew Orlou meant her to understand. She had noticed again and again that when she thought she was alone at Far Félice Orlou would appear, turning the corner of some hedged alley in the shadowy gardens.

Lawrence had spoken of it several times. "Does she always just materialize out of the ground, like that?"

"I never know how she arrives. It's a long walk up the levee. But you see, there she is."

"She gives me the creeps."

"Orlou is looking after us, that is all."

"You don't mean that, really, do you?"

Victoria said nothing, but she knew that Orlou was doing precisely that.

Again Lawrence had said: "Do you suppose that witch actually distrusts me?"

"You're a stranger."

Victoria was lying that time: she knew that she was the one Orlou distrusted.

Orlou and Phelia sat in Greenwood's back yard under the shade of a wide-spreading chinaberry tree. Phelia smoked a short-stemmed corncob pipe and made only monosyllabic answers to most of Orlou's questions. Her black eyes were inscrutable. She knew why Orlou was at Far Félice today, and Orlou knew that she knew. Both of them kept rigidly the convention of a polite visit.

Phelia was copper-colored, impassive, and old. She had been born on Far Félice lands and was distantly related to Orlou.

Conversation between the two followed a familiar pattern. It was almost like a ritual.

"How's Cap'n Julien these days, Orlou?" Phelia, like Orlou, had seen house service, and spoke much better than the average Negro.

"He's well, thank you, Phelia."

"He ain't mind the heat?"

"No."

"No, he never did. Ain't the folks goin' to Ponchartrain pretty soon?"

"They're talking about it."

"Nex' week be the first of June."

"Since Miss Lucie stays at Wyandotte we're always slow getting started."

"Ain't she comin' home from Wyandotte sometime?"

"She's just visiting."

"Ten years."

"Yes. Don't you remember about Mister Octave? He went to L'Heure Exquise to spend the summer——"

"An' stayed fourteen years. Yes, I know. Miss Lucie's different."

"Yes."

"She love White Cloud."

"Yes."

The two women were silent again, but each knew the conversation continued. Phelia knocked the coals from her pipe with an air of exasperation. Orlou answered by smoothing her stiff-starched dress with little pats of resignation and reassurance.

Phelia filled her pipe, stirred the ashes under the washpot for a live coal, and puffed with clear interrogation.

"Mr. Niles, he's well, I reckon."

"Oh, yes."

"How's Miss Flora?"

"She's all right." Orlou understood perfectly the juxtaposition of these names. Phelia nodded. She had received the reassurance she had asked.

"I guess nobody don't hear nothin' 'bout Mr. John no more?"

"No, indeed."

Phelia nodded. Orlou's tone said distinctly that no one wished to hear, and that no one would ever make an inquiry.

The drowsy summer afternoon hours went slowly. The slow-paced questions and the deliberate answers were exchanged one by one with full pauses to permit their exploration and assimilation. The shadows stretched out across the bare yard, and a faint dampish coolness came in from the river.

"Orlou, I ain't easy 'bout this."

Orlou sat motionless as stone. She did not move a finger or change expression.

Phelia went on. "I keep rememberin' the old-time stories 'bout the house." She glanced sideways toward the big house drowsing in the sun.

"The Far Félice people are all dead and gone, Phelia. The stories are dead and gone, too."

"The ghosts ain't dead, Orlou."

Orlou had been looking away. She glanced back quickly, but she did not speak.

"Seems to me sometimes lak I jes' seein' ghosts walkin' in that garden."

"I'm always here, Phelia."

"I know it, Orlou. I know it. But yo' gran'ma Jubilee was here, too."

"Yes."

"An' all the same——"

"It was a lie, Phelia."

"I don't know."

"Grandma Jubilee said so."

"You'd a said so, too. An' me too, if I'd a been there an' anybody ask me."

"Yes, but Grandma Jubilee told the truth. My own mother told me, Phelia, before she died. The story was a lie."

"Mr. Quintin Grandolet an' Mr. Paul kill each other."

"Yes."

"Sometimes I jes' think I see Miss Jeannette herself walkin' up an' down in there."

"I'm here."

"Yes. That's why I ain't so easy 'bout it."

"Why?"

"You know what I mean. What you here for?"

Orlou didn't answer.

"Orlou, you walkin' in old Jubilee's tracks right now."

"It was a lie, Phelia. Mr. Julien——"

"I ain't say nothin' 'bout Cap'n Julien. He certainly is Grandolet."

"Yes."

"One way or 'nother."

"Well, make your mind easy, Phelia."

"I ain't easy. I'm skeered."

"Phelia!"

"Yes."

"Do you know anything?"

"I ain't know nothin'."

"Well, then——"

"I jes' *feel*. Since 'way back in slavery times Far Félice been standin' there, rottin' to pieces. The Grandolets stay 'way fum it, clean away. Cap'n Julien, Mr. Jules when he was livin', an' Mr. Niles. All the time Mr. Niles was growin' up he ain't been inside that house more'n two, three times. Nobody want to go in there. Far Félice was bad luck. Bes' stay away fum bad-luck places."

"White folks don't believe in those things, Phelia."

"Orlou, you an' me got plenty good reason to know what white folks think. They ain't know ever'thing."

"I'm here, Phelia. You're here, too, and Greenwood."

"Greenwood, he worried."

"What does he say?"

"He say Far Félice all dress' up foh trouble!"

Phelia filled her pipe again, but the coals under the washpot had died out. She fumbled in her skirt pocket for a match.

Looking through the blue smoke at Orlou, she said, "Supposin' all that old-time story 'bout Miss Jeannette an' Mr. Paul *is* a lie."

"Well, then, it's a lie."

"Yo' gran'ma Jubilee she stay 'round, too, jes' lak you. She keep 'em apart. They was young folks. Young folks got hot blood, 'specially Grandolets an' Vélazys. Old Jubilee keep 'em apart."

Orlou looked steadily, unwinkingly, at Phelia.

"Old people always say how sperrits come back 'cause they ain't satisfy."

"We're not talking about spirits, Phelia."

"Sperrits could be whisperin' to other folks."

"Oh, Phelia!"

" 'Tain't far from the Grandolet buryin' ground up here to the house, Orlou."

"In another year or two, I think, I can call the restoration complete—at least it will be as good as I can make it." Victoria stood at the door of a latticed summer house looking across the length of the gardens and toward the façade of the house.

"You've enjoyed doing it, haven't you? Collecting the furniture and all?" Dr. Gaynes asked the question absently.

"Yes. More than I can tell you."

"Why?"

"I don't know, really. It has been an exercise in fancy, maybe that is it."

"You wanted Far Félice back again, didn't you?"

"That's an understanding remark, Lawrence. But of course you understand everything. Yes, I wanted Far Félice back again. It was nearly gone."

"I'm still curious about a lot of things, Victoria. Why *did* you want it back?"

"Just interest in an old place, perhaps. I hate to see any of them go."

"That isn't it. Maybe because it belongs to you?"

"No, Lawrence. I belong to it."

"I've seen places that have the same feel—I guess you'd say atmosphere—as this."

"Really? But where?"

"France. The beautiful little château at Chantilly has it. Versailles, too——"

"Oh, but they——"

"I know what you are going to say. They're sumptuous. Yes, but—they have also the same look of having been witnesses of something gay and hapless. They're haunted."

Victoria nodded. "Maybe. I can imagine. Certainly this is haunted by one's own imagination. Hippolyte d'Aupais walked up and down this same *allée couverte*. Quintin Grandolet walked here, too, and his distracted wife. You said 'gay and hapless.' That's what they were, all of them, and the sense of their haplessness is heavy on the place. One thing I feel, though, that I never quite explain to myself."

"What is that? I thought you were always ready with explanations from beyond the beyond." He smiled, his tone bantering.

"Oh, Lawrence! I know pretty well why one feels many things in these places. It all comes out of oneself, or—out of one's reception of something that tries to come through."

Dr. Gaynes laughed. "There! That is what I mean."

She ignored this. "I was going to mention the one special quality that I believe a few places have. It's a sense of waiting."

"Waiting? Um—yes, but——"

"Is that the way the gardens at Versailles or the châteaux of the Loire feel?"

"No."

"Aren't they just the shells, the mementos?"

"I think so."

"You don't feel that their story is unfinished?"

"No."

"Well, what I feel here, especially at Far Félice, is that the story isn't finished."

"And so, here at Far Félice, you are resetting the stage?"

Victoria did not answer. She was remembering something suddenly. It was the sound of Niles' voice saying: "Make no mistake, Victoria. We came too late. The show is over." She shook the recollection away with an impatient shrug.

The lovely, ordered garden lay dreaming and impassive. There was, Dr. Gaynes thought, a quite special pathos about it. It was such a lonely garden, set off here in the wilderness. Maybe it did have for that reason a look of waiting. Yes, come to think of it, that word did pretty well describe it.

They walked slowly, aware of each other, but allowing their thoughts to drift. The air was warm, and as sweet as honey. The last fallen blossoms of the azaleas lay fading on the ground. But a dozen cloying perfumes hung in the air with a druglike heaviness. Many small murmurs made themselves apparent, but they only emphasized the wide-spreading stillness, and the remoteness of the place. The muted zoom of a bumblebee, the faint whirr of a dragonfly passing close, the tiny crackle of a small grasshopper, the thin creak of a beetle startled into flight, the vanish of a bird cry overhead, and occasionally the echo of a call or a laugh from the quarters quickly lost again as if the silence itself smothered the sound.

Victoria was still thinking of her own description of the

peculiar spell which seemed to intensify as one dwelt upon it. A sense of waiting.

Lawrence was thinking, too. But he was thinking that this fine old house should not be standing empty and unused. These enchanting gardens should not lie here under sun, under moon, deserted.

The looming presence of the house dramatized the two people walking back and forth through the patterned maze of pathways. Both of them were aware of the singular compulsion to rise to the mysterious demands of the place and the curious spell of the hour.

Victoria knew bitterly well what had happened to her. She was vaguely aware, too, that it had happened here at Far Félice. She resented the clamor of her flesh, but she went dizzily forward, fascinated and drawn by the vertiginous whirl of her emotions. It seemed to her that the moments, here, now as she moved, gave way before her, sweeping the solid ground from under her feet.

She no longer asked herself what would happen, but when.

Lawrence was plagued by the old feeling he had experienced when he first met Victoria. It was the feeling that she expected him to be interesting, exceptional, dramatic—a coactor with her in a scene which he did not understand. A sort of embarrassment, rather boyish, a bit sheepish, came over him. He kept silent and covered his unease with a stiff reserve which Victoria mistook for renunciation and control. Just now she viewed that conclusion with a shade of relief. She wanted him to want her, she wanted him to want her more than she wanted him. If she could know that, and see that, it might lessen her own passion. She could fall back more endurably into her own centered concept of unprofaned aloofness. Her blood made protest, but from far back in the dark of her unconscious, the effort held. It kept her, for the moment at least, from breakdown. If only she could accept the shadow for the reality. If only she could go on and on playing near, perhaps nearer and nearer, to surrender——

Lawrence was wondering now. Perhaps he was a fool. Certainly he was not untouched by Victoria's charm and what to his realistic physician's eye was her apparent willingness to go the whole way in this teasing, tantalizing, half-yes, half-no, game. He wondered if she was also playing the game with herself. Was she not quite willing? Or was she waiting for his move? Was he being just a little bit inadequate as a male that he still hesitated?

Did he really want her? At times, certainly. Did all of this strike through to any deep need of her? Did it threaten really a shattering emotional crisis? He knew that it did not. All of this—this play—had been very pretty indeed. He had enjoyed it. He was enjoying it now. It relieved the humdrum of existence. There was glamour in it. Yes, that was it! Glamour. The mind and imagination can always enjoy glamour for its own sake, make good psychic use of it. It sustained a kind of hidden self that would scarcely admit openly the need for this colorful nourishment. But he was not prepared to court disaster for the sake of it.

Nevertheless he knew, and he knew well, the sudden pitfalls there might be in this artificially charged relationship. They were consciously, purposely walking on the fine edge of danger, trying for the thrill of it.

Victoria stopped suddenly, faced him, and put her hands on his arms.

"Lawrence!"

"Careful, Victoria——"

"What?"

"Orlou."

She dropped her hands to her sides and moved away. At the
end of the overarched path, Orlou walked slowly across the
open space.

SIXTEEN

Niles' rooms in the north wing of White Cloud were severely bare of all but the simplest comforts. The front room had several filing cabinets ranged along the wall, and down the center of the long room stood a huge table heaped with books, pamphlets, and papers of all kinds.

He sat at this table working on some sheets of figures, while Q-G watched him. Q-G balanced himself on the arm of a chair. From time to time he lost his precarious position and fell back into the seat, or came down on the floor with a resounding thump.

Niles looked up. "You're going to break your one and only neck, son."

Q-G laughed. Presently Niles pushed the papers away and lighted a cigarette. The two of them regarded each other for several minutes without speaking.

Q-G attempted a circumpass of the chair without touching the floor. This involved squirming under the arm, walking on the rungs, and other surprising contortions.

"As I said——"

"I'm going to break my one and only neck."

"Yes."

Q-G subsided. "I guess the Grandolets are pretty wonderful people, aren't they?"

"Whatever put that idea into your head?"

"Well, aren't they, really?"

"No."

"Honest?"

"No."

"Isn't Grandfather Julien wonderful?"

"Yes, of course."

"Isn't Aunt Lucie wonderful?"

"Certainly."

"And Cousin Flora?"

"Yes."

Q-G grinned. He took two long steps toward his father, seized him by the ears, and kissed him on both cheeks. This was a demonstration which by mutual consent they reserved for their private encounters.

"Well, you're certainly wonderful." Q-G wagged his head. Niles made a very serious face. "Undoubtedly."

"Well, then! Just like I said, I guess the Grandolets are pretty wonderful people. You say so yourself."

"I'm afraid that's an incurable habit of ours, Q-G. But I hadn't expected you to develop the idea so soon."

"Don't talk grown-up, please, sir."

"Was that too grown-up for you? Didn't you understand every word I said?"

"Yes."

"Well, then."

"It just sounded—top-lofty."

"Where'd you get that word?"

"Grandfather Julien."

"Oh. But now about the Grandolets. They're not really

[263]

wonderful, Q-G. I shouldn't want you to have that idea."

"But, one by one——"

"Yes, and you might remember that your mother is wonderful, too."

"Yes. And she's pretty."

"Very. You can be proud to have such a pretty mother."

Q-G kept an absolutely blank expression. His wide brown eyes did not blink. For a moment he looked surprisingly like Grandfather Julien. Niles glanced away.

"The Grandolets are just people."

"But they're not like the Wards."

"Just a difference in fortunes, that's all."

"Are we rich?"

"No."

"You said——"

"The Wards are not property owners. But they're good people—just as good as we are."

"Grandfather Julien doesn't think so."

"How do you know that?"

"He doesn't invite Mr. Ward into the house."

"Just custom. Q-G, some people occupy a more fortunate position than others, but they're not fundamentally any better than anybody else."

"Do you believe that?"

Niles smiled in spite of his efforts not to. "Almost," he said weakly.

"Aha! I bet you think the Grandolets are pretty wonderful."

"No matter what anybody thinks, they're not."

"I think everybody around here thinks so. I bet you even think I am."

"That's a trick. I like you."

"But aren't I a real Grandolet?"

"Of course."

Q-G sighed contentedly.

"Son, what do you really want to be when you grow up?"

"A planter, like you, and run White Cloud."

"Wouldn't like to be a lawyer?"

"Like Mr. Carrington?"

"Yes."

"No."

"Nor a doctor?"

Q-G made a face. "I'd like to know about everything that grows, like Grandfather Julien does. He reads to me out of botany books and then we look for things."

"You like that?"

"Ver-ry much."

Niles noticed the throaty pronunciation. "Do you like to speak French?"

"Yes."

"I think that's fine. It's a Grandolet tradition—since you admire the family so much."

"Oh, I'll do whatever the Grandolets usually do."

Niles' eyes twinkled. "Your tone of voice when you say 'the Grandolets' is just a shade too regal."

"What's that?"

"Royal. Like kings."

"I guess they could have been kings if they'd wanted to. I guess they could have been kings of Louisiana."

"I rather think some of them thought they were."

"Sure enough."

"They acted that way."

"Nice?"

"No. Top-lofty."

"I see. If you're a king you don't *have* to act like one."

"Or a Grandolet."

"Making fun?" Q-G's eyes amplified the question. Their laconic exchanges were also a private habit. Q-G felt it was very man to man. "Are you?"

"Yes."

"Why?"

"Because you are funny. Do you know what I think you had better do?"

"Is it disagreeable?"

"Maybe."

"Oh."

"I think you'd better go to boarding school this fall."

Q-G sighed. "Grandfather Julien says so, too."

"Oh, he does?"

"Yes. We talked about it last week."

"Um."

"He thought he'd better explain to me about boys and girls."

"What about 'em?"

"You know. The way it says 'sex relations' in the book."

"Oh, of course, of course. You didn't know about that?"

"Not much. I guessed some. Grandfather Julien made it ver-ry clear—with rabbits."

"Yes, yes. Naturally. Rabbits. Oh, certainly."

"Are you embarrassed?"

"Who? Me?"

"Grandfather said one shouldn't be embarrassed. It's natural. Only not to talk about it."

"That's quite right."

"He explained about gentlemen, too."

"Really?"

"Only he said afterward mighty damn few of them act that way."

"*What?*"

"I think he was kind of talking to himself then."

Niles took a deep breath. The look of half wonder in his eye was genuine.

"He thought I ought to know everything before I went to school."

"Oh, quite so."

"I guess I'll be going to St. Xavier, won't I, just like you?"

"Yes, son. It seems you've arranged most of it."

Q-G nodded. "School opens October first this year."

"Did you tell your mother?"

Q-G shook his head.

"Well, I would. You should have her permission, I think."

Q-G resumed his acrobatics on the chair. "She won't like it."

"You think not?"

The boy shook his head again.

Niles arose and with a sudden wave of emotion gathered Q-G into his arms and held him tight. Q-G held perfectly still for a moment, then he reached up and twisted Niles' hair into two threatening horns, and vigorously rubbed noses.

Victoria had never felt that her son belonged to her. He had been reared by Pinky, by Orlou, by Niles, and by Grandfather Julien. Her relationship with him had been kept on a sort of picture-book plane. He asked permissions of her and she granted them. She selected clothes for him. She read to him. He was polite to her. But his confidence and the outpourings of affection of childhood were for others. She readily delegated the monotonous, repetitive cares to them. She readily accepted part in the more picturesque tableaux. She liked to introduce him, to say, "This is my son, Julien Quintin." She liked the sight of him. She had been content with these casual conjunctions.

Q-G! There was much about him that reminded her of the very quality of White Cloud itself. The word "patrician" came to her, and with it those other related words, "reticent," "remote."

Victoria was more alone that summer than she had been any year since she had come to White Cloud. The weather was hot, and she heard little from Wyandotte. Niles was away much of the time on business. Q-G was occupied with his lessons. Grandfather Julien seemed to withdraw more and more from a living world. He was querulous at times, and preferred to be alone.

Lawrence came less often to White Cloud. Occasionally he brought someone with him. He was not looking well, Victoria thought. He was strained and haggard.

"Are you quite well, Lawrence?" she asked him one day.

"Oh, I don't know. I suppose so."

"Surely you know."

"Things have been pretty tense."

"How? What do you mean?"

"At home."

"Oh."

"I may as well tell you, Victoria. Marian has left me."

"Marian—left——"

"Yes. No one really knows it. She's on a visit in Ohio."

"Because—of——"

"Yes. Because of us."

"I suppose I should be sorry."

"No. Don't lie. You don't care, and I'm not sure I do."

"If you're not sure, then——"

"Victoria, there's something between married people that can't just be ignored, or thrown away, or broken off without, well, a kind of injury. It's like losing a hand. You can live, but you are crippled."

"Maybe I understand, maybe not."

"Probably not. You are different. You are a kind of unmarriable person."

"I don't know what you mean by that."

"No matter. I—I don't know what to do. I can't think of—really giving you up. That's a queer thing to say when you aren't mine—in any sense."

"I don't know what I can do without you, Lawrence."

"There's a practical side, too."

"Oh, I see. I guess I do."

"I won't have any practice. Medicine is a sensitive profession."

"Have you noticed a difference?"

"Yes."

"Then there has been more talk than we knew."

"Talk! According to Marian, there's been a hell of a lot of it. Victoria, God knows what you are to me, but I think I need you. You've been a kind of magic, something wonderful—a whole enchanted world. There's been nothing between us but words—nothing but words. I don't know how long that can last. We are flesh and blood. I am, anyway. But sometimes I think I could go on with—with just seeing you."

She laid her hand on his arm. "Go home. Let's think. I've never said I love you. I guess we're insane. I don't know, I don't know. Only don't leave me entirely—not yet."

"Grandfather Julien, I'm going to drive up to Far Félice. Won't you change your mind and come along?"

"No, Victoria, thank you."

"Oh, come now! It's a beautiful day. It will do you good."

"I shall never go to Far Félice, Victoria, until I die."

Her face darkened. "Isn't it time, after nearly a century, to forget? Far Félice is just a place, a house, a garden. It's quite beautiful now."

"No, Victoria. Thank you."

She drove her small car through the swamp road toward Far Félice. The day was heavenly. It would be fun to have someone to talk with, to laugh a little. This was life, this day, this sunshine, this ecstasy of birds and vivid blooming flowers. Poor Grandfather Julien. Her invitation had probably set him to brooding.

She skirted the Grandolet cemetery. The vaults and tombs had been recently whitewashed and the place tidied. The sun made patterns of moving light on the snowy brick walls, the air was light and fragrant, the birds flew gaily above it. It seemed a cheerful place. There they were, the old Grandolets. She felt friendly toward them.

Far Félice was a blaze of bright colors. Such a pity that it lay here with no one to see. She wandered about the gardens most of the afternoon. Once she went up to the levee to look at the river. High summer stood in the land like a green, still fire.

For the first time in her life she fell into dreams about her real parents. It was strange not to know who they were, their names, their place. Had they been married? Did they die suddenly, leaving her? Or, was she simply unwanted? Were they perhaps two helpless, mad young lovers caught in the spell of a feverish long-ago spring?

For the first time she did not think of herself left with bitter questions and the long aftermath. For the first time she thought with something like tenderness of those unknown lovers who loved perhaps in wretchedness and revolt.

. . . Jeannette Vélazy . . . her nameless mother . . . and now Victoria Grandolet. Were they of one company?

The light was failing when she decided to go home. She stopped to inspect the *pigeonnier*. Greenwood had repaired the broken coping.

"Victoria!"

She started. "Oh, Lawrence! You here? I didn't hear a car."

"I've been here a long time."

Something desperate in his voice disturbed her.

"What's the matter? Has something happened?"

"No. Nothing. Let's go in the house."

"It's late, Lawrence, and—and Greenwood is working somewhere about the place."

"I have to talk to you."

"All right. Let's go in the front way."

Lawrence stopped in the hall. There was a musty smell about it, and most of the furniture was shrouded.

"We've had happy hours here, talking and planning. Haven't we, Victoria?"

"Why do you talk like that?"

"I'm going away."

She felt her knees sag a little. "Oh, Lawrence."

"I've got to."

"Where are you going?"

"I'm giving up my practice here—what there is of it. I'm going North, somewhere."

"To—to her?"

"I'm going to get her back."

"She—she's more important to you than—than I am?"

"I don't know. I can't——"

[271]

"You can't let her go?"

"Something like that, I guess."

"But you can let me go?"

"You don't belong to me. You couldn't, you wouldn't, anyway."

"I——"

"Don't lie, my dear. Just say you love me, and let me go."

"I shall be alone now, Lawrence. I shall have no one."

He took her by the arms and drew her roughly to him.

"Kiss me, Victoria."

"Yes, yes——"

For a moment they stood there while the world swung crazily away from them.

Victoria was startled by a sound. She thrust Lawrence away, and stared, wide-eyed, unbelieving, and utterly aghast. Q-G was standing a few steps above them on the curving stairway. His face was as white and still as stone, but his narrowed eyes blazed. He took another step down leaning toward the balustrade with both of his childish hands clutching the slender rail. Neither Victoria nor Lawrence moved.

Q-G came down another step. *My father will kill you—both of you,* he said. Then he ran down the steps and tugged at the door.

Victoria broke from her trance. "Q-G! Wait a minute!"

He turned, struggling not to cry, but his mouth twisted dreadfully. "Let me alone! Let me alone!" he shouted.

Victoria turned toward Lawrence. "You must go, quickly."

He did not move at once. "I suppose he will, too."

"Will what?"

"Niles Grandolet will kill us—both of us."

She turned heavily to the door. "I suppose so." Her voice

sounded dull, disinterested. He followed her, carefully closing the door of Far Félice behind them.

"Supper's ready, Miss Victoria."

"Thank you, Emsy."

Grandfather Julien was waiting. They sat down together.

"Heard from Niles today, Victoria?"

"No, I haven't."

"I had a card late this afternoon. He's going to stay over in Shreveport for a couple more days."

"Anything more?"

"No, just a few words."

"Emsy, where is Q-G?"

"He asked if he could have his supper sent up to his rooms. Yes'm."

"What's the matter with him, Victoria, sick?"

"No. Probably didn't wish to dress."

"He should come to meals."

"He usually does, Grandfather."

"I hope Niles can straighten out some of his affairs this trip. I guess he's worried, Victoria."

She looked up quickly. "Why? What is it?"

Grandfather Julien flashed a keen and surprised look of inquiry across the table. "Hasn't he talked to you lately?"

"About what?"

"Business."

"He never does, Grandfather."

"Why? You're his wife."

"He always says, 'Don't bother your head, leave those things to me.'"

"That's wrong of him."

"Perhaps. I don't understand much about the affairs of the place."

"That's because you haven't been advised. You know that Niles is in debt?"

Her fork slipped from her fingers. "No, I didn't."

"White Cloud is doubly mortgaged, Victoria. I thought this afternoon you should be told not to plan anything further at Far Félice."

"Why wasn't I told? Mortgaged!"

"Fortunately, it's all in the family. There's no danger of losing the place. He'll pull out in time."

"All in the family?"

"Yes. Flora lent him the money."

"White Cloud is mortgaged to Flora?"

"Yes. But as I said, there's no danger."

Flora! Victoria's face flamed. Flora! How like all of them to tell her nothing! But her dismay over this situation burned quickly away in the deadly fire of greater dangers.

After supper she debated what she should do. Go up and see Q-G and try to make some casual explanation? No. Q-G was oddly precocious. He was still a child but he must have understood what he saw. She was also sure that he meant to talk to Niles. In that he would be actuated by a special kind of loyalty—a loyalty to Niles, to White Cloud, to the family which grimly set her outside of consideration. It was this exclusion of her from any protective action that thrust her away and far from that close-knit abstraction of family which clearly Q-G thought of as concerning Niles and himself more than it did her.

She knew now that the furious, morbid passion she had felt for Lawrence Gaynes was dead. It died in that instant she had looked up to see the stricken face of Q-G leaning over them.

She swept all thought of Lawrence from her mind. She tried to collect what elements of safety might remain, but she could find none.

She had said: "I shall be alone, now, Lawrence. I shall have no one." The words came back in derisive echo. A few hours ago she had said that. But she had had everything then. She had even had her son. It was now, at this moment, that she could say she was alone.

She lifted the curtain, opened a window, and went out on the gallery. There was a light in Niles' rooms. That meant Q-G had gone over there for the night. He had turned away in this symbolic fashion from her, from the roof over her.

A pale twilight lingered. The distant curve of the river was dim and misty. There would be a full moon later.

She went back into the house but the room smothered her. She decided to go to the belvedere. She must have space to breathe. She must try somehow to think. Passing the whispering column she shrank to one side.

It was suffocatingly hot on the upper gallery. She opened the door at the end of the last narrow stairway and stepped out on the roof. Absently she opened several of the French windows around the belvedere. A rush of warm air poured out.

It was very still outside. Above the trees, far over the east bank, there was a lightening of the sky where presently the moon would rise. The gardens lay black and silent in the dense shadows.

Victoria walked restlessly back and forth. She had to tell herself, first, that she was not frightened. Q-G had seen what he had seen. She would say to Niles in the plainest terms what that had been. He could do what he wished. She could honestly be indifferent at this moment what that might be. But it was the deadly humiliation of what would be thought, what was undoubtedly already thought, and talked of. The three women at Wyandotte. They had drawn together, away from her, against her. Did she fully deserve that?

Victoria Grandolet of White Cloud . . . Victoria Grandolet of White Cloud . . .

Her brain was saying that over and over, as if it were summoning her, warning her, accusing her, trying her.

Maybe she wouldn't be Victoria Grandolet of White Cloud any more. Maybe she wouldn't even be Victoria Grandolet. Then she wouldn't be anybody. It was the only thing she had ever been, but maybe even at that there had never really been such a person. She had been an imitation. She had been an imitation Grandolet. She had been an imitation wife. She tried to avoid, to back away from this shower of denunciations coming from she knew not where. Imitation—imitation—imitation. Imitation lady. *Imitation woman!*

Revelation and confusion and self-pity, and bitter consciousness of the harsh realities of her situation, rose to a dreadful crescendo in her mind. To it was added this new hateful knowledge—White Cloud in debt to Flora! Even her Far Félice project—probably paid for with Flora's money. If Flora, and those two whispering and conspiring women at Wyandotte, had only been friendly to her! Was it *her* fault?

Victoria had not made herself clearsighted and ruthless and icily accurate for nothing. Those very faculties turned full force against her. The acting was over. The make-believe was finished.

The moon arose and floated clear of the cloud of trees to the east. Its light flooded the façades of the north and south wings, both clearly visible from the roof. How still they were, those stark white columns, and how indifferent! They had stood so through all the years, through disaster and defeat and death, through spring and summer and winter. There they stood while her world was crashing into dust.

What if Orlou were right? *White Cloud won't take what it don't like. No matter who it is, if this house don't like some-body, it won't take him in. It'll destroy him first.*

How often she had quoted that. How often she had used it against people she didn't like, people who seemed uncomfortable here.

White Cloud rejects ...

White Cloud rejects ...

Orlou had been right. Victoria felt that she had always known it was true. It was true. It was true. At this moment she had been thrust away from it, all that was in it, animate and inanimate, Niles, her son, the ancient spirit of the Grando-lets, had rejected her.

She pressed the back of her hand against her mouth and began to cry. She must go somewhere, she must do something. She must save something, someway, and maybe herself. She must see someone, talk to someone.

She dropped her shawl and hurried toward the stair. She would see Q-G, yes, she would make him see. She would make everyone see. They must see. They had liked her once. She was Victoria, wasn't she? She was Niles' wife, she was Q-G's mother. No one had really understood. She would tell them. They would help.

She turned away from the night. The rows of opened windows confused her. Which was the door?

... They would help, surely. Grandfather Julien, Aunt Lucie ... Niles ... Q-G ... *Flora!*

She stepped blindly forward.

A long wavering cry sounded throughout the house and then a shattering crash. Orlou ran from Victoria's dressing room to the balustrade. The great chandelier was wheeling in wide, eccentric circles, half of its crystal chains hanging. Victoria lay on the black and white marble floor, her white dress a welter of red. She lay quite still, huddled in a scattered mass of glittering, broken crystals.

A second cry rang through the galleries. It was Orlou this time, but before anyone could come she was bending over the broken and slashed body of her mistress. She tore off her apron and wrapped it about Victoria's face.

"Orlou—my God, what has happened?"

"Don't look, Mr. Julien! Miss Victoria fell from up there somewhere. She's dead, Mr. Julien."

The old man staggered back a few steps. "Orlou, are you sure? Call the doctor, quick."

"She's dead, Mr. Julien. She's cut all to pieces." Orlou pointed to the chandelier, still dancing crazily above them. "She fell through that."

The servants were running into the hall. Grandfather Julien spoke sharply. "Emsy, call Dr. Gaynes, and then try to get Mr. Niles for me. He's at Shreveport. Pinky, help Orlou carry Miss Victoria—in there." He pointed to the library. "And, Luther——"

"Yes, sir."

Grandfather Julien pointed at the chandelier. "Stop that damn thing swinging, will you? And——"

"Yes, sir."

"Go upstairs and don't let Q-G come down. Tell somebody to wash up this floor. Quick, now."

Orlou laid a handful of white flowers inside the coffin beside Victoria's masked face. She looked across the room at Aunt Lucie and Flora.

"No, ma'am. We don't have to say so. It ought to stay in the family, but I know it wasn't an accident."

Flora caught her breath in a horrified gasp. "Orlou, how can you make a statement like that? Do you know what you are saying?"

"Yes, ma'am. I'm saying Miss Victoria killed herself."

"Orlou, this is serious. You had better be very careful. What did you see?"

"I didn't see anything. Only—Miss Flora, I've been with Miss Victoria since the day she came to White Cloud. There was two people in her, plain as day."

Aunt Lucie held up her hand. "Stop it, Orlou. I don't want to have that kind of talk in this room over Victoria's coffin. I won't have it."

"I knew her better'n anybody, Miss Lucie. I'm not saying anything against her—not against Miss Victoria. I've been with her through everything. She wasn't one to talk, but I always knew what was going on. There was two of her."

"I wish you would stop saying that. It's silly." Aunt Lucie arose.

"I just want to say for her what I think she couldn't ever say for herself. There was two of her. One of them hated the other. It was that other one that White Cloud wouldn't have. Miss Victoria somehow, inside of herself, hated that one, even if it was part of herself. She had to destroy that one. That's how it happened."

Aunt Lucie sat down again, but just for a moment. "That's some sort of superstitious nonsense, Orlou. I wouldn't want Q-G ever to hear a whisper of anything like it."

Orlou did not move. She stood over Victoria like a priestess. There was something suddenly protective in her attitude.

"Miss Lucie, I never did pass on anything in the Grandolet

family that could do anybody any harm. I never will. I'm just saying that in one way Miss Victoria belonged to White Cloud, in another way she didn't. That's why she had to die. Yes'm."

The funeral services in the drawing room were over. Grandfather Julien came slowly into the library where the family was waiting. He looked exceedingly frail. He sat down heavily and crossed his thin fine hands on the crook of his cane. He glanced about at them. Marie Vélazy, Lucie, Flora, and Niles.

"Where is Q-G?"

"He went upstairs, Father." Aunt Lucie twisted her damp handkerchief. "You can't talk to him. He won't answer. He just sits and looks out of the window. I declare he looks old all at once."

Julien nodded and sighed. He spoke presently as if he were talking to himself.

"We never knew her, I guess. She was always a stranger. We didn't know her people, we didn't know the place she came from, we didn't even know what she liked or didn't like. She could have come from another planet for all we ever knew. Maybe we wouldn't have been at home where she came from. Maybe she had to be a stranger here. I never knew anything about her. Maybe Q-G will look back and understand her someday. He has her in his blood."

He paused. "She was very beautiful," he added.

There was a stir in the hall. Q-G came in. Niles arose.

"Come," he said. "It's time to go."

They stood grouped near the front door, as the gray-velvet coffin was borne through the hall. Niles looked about him. It seemed only yesterday that he had brought her here. Everything looked the same now as it did then. The doors at the back were filled with wide-eyed servants. On the landing Orlou stood, stiff and straight, as motionless as a statue.

Aunt Lucie at the door spoke suddenly to the pallbearers. "Not that stairway! The other one. The dead always go out by the right."

Q-G clung to Grandfather Julien. His face was stony still and stiff. There was a new look in his eyes. It was the look of guardianship. Whatever lay behind it was inviolate. All of the Grandolets had that look.

The cortege started, turned into the levee road, and moved toward Far Félice.

Niles looked back. White Cloud stood like a dream in the quiet park. He noticed that the shutters of Victoria's rooms were closed. The road curved and the gray banners of moss shut the house from view. Here under the trees it seemed to be already dark.

ABOUT THE AUTHOR

Henry Bellamann has had a varied career. He has served as acting director and chairman of the examining board of the Juilliard Musical Foundation, dean of the Curtis Institute of Music at Philadelphia, and professor of music at Vassar College. France made him a Chevalier of the Legion of Honor, and DePauw University gave him an honorary musical doctorate.

He teaches and practices the piano, collects stamps, old furniture, and rare Danteana. At odd times he works at a translation of the *Divina Commedia.*

The best-selling novels, *Kings Row* and *Floods of Spring,* were published in 1940 and 1942, respectively. Previous books were *Cups of Illusion* and *The Upward Pass* (both poetry) and the novels *Petenera's Daughter, Crescendo,* and *The Richest Woman in Town.*